MASONIC COMMUNITY
UTICA, N.Y. 13501

HOW THE IRISH BUILT THE ERIE

by

HARVEY CHALMERS II

BOOKMAN ASSOCIATES, INC.
NEW YORK

RETURN TO
ACACIA VILLAGE LIBRARY
A MASONIC COMMUNITY
UTICA, N.Y. 13501

Copyright © *1964 by Bookman Associates, Inc.*

ALL RIGHTS RESERVED

Library of Congress Catalog Card Number: 64-25061

Manufactured in the United States of America

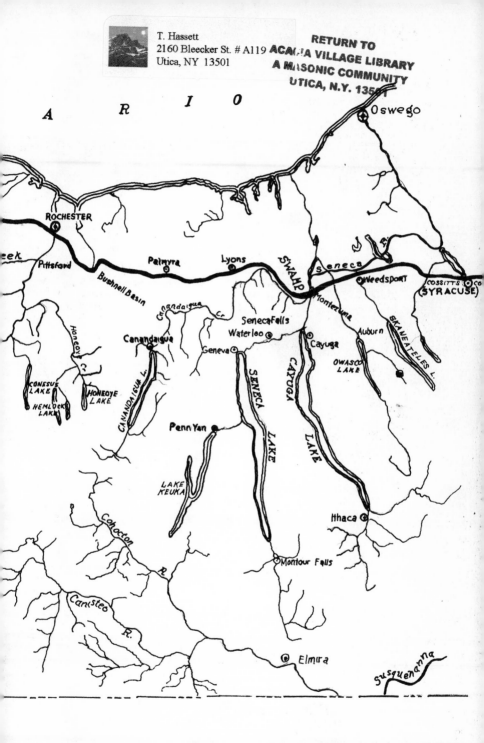

T. Hassett
2160 Bleecker St. # A119
Utica, NY 13501

RETURN TO
ACACIA VILLAGE LIBRARY
A MASONIC COMMUNITY
UTICA, N.Y. 13501

RETURN TO
LA VILLAGE LIBRARY
MASONIC COMMUNITY
UTICA, N.Y. 13501

RETURN TO
ACACIA VILLAGE LIBRARY
A MASONIC COMMUNITY
UTICA, N.Y. 13501

HOW THE IRISH BUILT THE ERIE

Property of Acacia Village

Library

Given by:

Peg Hassett

In Memory of:

T. Hassett

Date: *Aug. 11, 2003*

RETURN TO
ACACIA VILLAGE LIBRARY
A MASONIC COMMUNITY
UTICA, N.Y. 13501

For Arthur A. Chalmers—my father
Of whose achievements I am justly proud

ACKNOWLEDGMENTS

FRED GILLEN, Tribes Hill, N.Y., Senior Civil Engineer Retired, N.Y. State Dept. of Engineers

JOHN G. BROUGHTON, Principal Scientist and State Geologist, Albany, N.Y.

NORMAN B. WILKINSON, Research Associate, Hagley Museum, Wilmington, Del.

DOUGLAS OLCOTT, President, Mechanics and Farmers Bank, Albany, N.Y.

DONALD B. STEVENS, N.Y. State Engineer

A. H. BARBEN, President, Canal Society of N.Y. State, Seneca Falls, N.Y.

JACK ADAMS, Schoharie, N.Y., Manager, Cushing Stone Quarries

LESTER E. PARTELOW, Weedsport, N.Y.

DON NEGUS, Illustrator, Chittenango, N.Y.

JUDGE MATTHEW DUNNE, Troy, N.Y.

ALFRED T. GOBLE, Union College, Schenectady, N.Y.

FRANK THOMPSON, Curator, Weighlock Building, Canal Museum, Syracuse, N.Y.

CHANDLER KNIGHT, County Judge, Montgomery County, N.Y.

CONTENTS

CONTENTS

LIST OF ILLUSTRATIONS

Chapter 1

IN APRIL, 1817, when the long-pending Canal Act finally became the Canal Law through action of the New York State Legislature, Governor-elect DeWitt Clinton had at last mounted a political platform from which he might ascend to the White House in Washington, D.C. If the then-current President, James Monroe, were re-elected, as seemed likely, there were indications that the dynasty of United States Presidents from Virginia would run out in 1825. The next President would probably come from a northern state. The Canal Commissioners had said that they expected the canal to be completed by 1824 and operating in 1825. Predicating his hopes on this achievement DeWitt Clinton could reasonably expect to be nominated for President by the Clintonians, the remnant of the old Federalist Party, and his followers among the Conservative Republicans.

No one understood the potential of this situation better

than State Senator, Attorney General of New York, and ex-Regent Martin Van Buren, who had begun his career as taproom boy in a Kinderhook, New York, tavern. The tavern keeper, an irritable man, had trained Martin to be efficient in serving everyone and to be agreeable at all times regardless of drunken customers' demands and adverse circumstances. Under the tavern keeper's tutelage, "being agreeable" had become a way of life for Martin. It had stood him in good stead when he had been elected a delegate to the Congressional Caucus at Troy in 1800, and again three years later when he was admitted to the bar in New York City. It had won him the office of Surrogate for Columbia County in 1808 and kept him there until he had been elected to the State Senate in 1813.

With progress Van Buren had developed an alert mind which understood and appraised people according to their potential usefulness to him; his sunny smile disarmed them, and his friendly manner took them into captivity. He complied with the prevailing style of shaving to the extent of a clean upper lip and chin, but cultivated an arrangement of whiskers on his cheeks which covered the hard lines, and made him seem always to be in a pleasant humor, although the corners of his mouth turned down. Behind his merry eyes he was facile and clever, but he wasn't physically strong like Clinton.

DeWitt Clinton, through extensive and intensive education and training, had developed a mastery of English which he exercised with telling effect both by tongue and pen. In 1816 he founded the Literary and Philosophical Society. The next year he was founder and first president of the New York Historical Society, a member of the American Academy of Art, discoverer of a native American wheat, and a writer and lecturer on antiquities of western New York. So superior was his reputation as a duelist, that when he challenged Aaron Burr—which by the code entitled Burr to the choice of weapons—Burr prudently declined to fight.

Clinton would prepare an ambush for his political enemies and then drive them into it. Van Buren would dig a pitfall, cover it, and wait for his opponents to fall in.

In 1812, when Clinton was Peace Party candidate for United States President, Van Buren acted as his campaign manager. So efficiently did Van Buren function that if Clinton could have added a minority in the southern states to his majority in the north, he would probably have been elected President of the United States instead of James Madison.

Beneath his grumpy, autocratic exterior, Clinton was handicapped by a soft streak of sentiment. In contrast, Van Buren's engaging manner masked a coldly calculating mind. Thus, when the Canal Act was being debated in the State Senate in April, 1817, Van Buren, bitterest enemy of the canal, perceiving with keen political insight that there was little hope of stopping the act in the legislature, suddenly shifted to Clinton's side and made an enthusiastic speech in favor of the act. At the conclusion of that speech, Clinton, remembering how capably Van Buren had campaigned for him in 1812, became so aroused emotionally that he walked over to Van Buren, shook his hand, and thanked him warmly.

By that handshake Van Buren became convinced that Clinton had at last come to look upon him as a loyal and devoted follower who perhaps had been temporarily estranged by some of Clinton's jealous enemies. In other words, Van Buren had created for himself the role of spy, enabling him to learn by overhearing and by casual inquiry the progress and setbacks in the constructing of the canal— information which his followers could use in converting setbacks into near disaster! Clinton had, without knowing it, publicly and voluntarily offered Van Buren this opportunity.

Because the wrecking of canal construction and the undermining of Clinton's influence in the State Legislature must be done concomitantly, Van Buren obviously needed a small but efficient band of assistants. From Utica he chose a power-hungry, brilliant, young lawyer named Samuel Talcott, who had been a Federalist until that party merged with the Clintonians. He had then defected to the Bucktails* because of Clinton's arbitrary ways. By report his manners in court were almost clownish. Still whether he represented plaintiff or defendant he had never lost a case. He also lived in a locality well-situated for Van Buren's purpose, for canal construction would start at Rome, only twelve miles west of Utica. Van Buren believed that he could win Talcott by offering to make him State Attorney General as soon as that office were opened for a new appointment.

To fulfill such a promise Van Buren needed more power in the legislature. He had received an inkling that Joseph Ellicott, a canal commissioner, expected to resign from the board in the summer of 1818. Naturally Clinton would appoint a Clintonian to fill the vacancy. By expanding his influence Van Buren might defeat the ratification by his own party, the Bucktails, which incidentally would give them a majority on the Board of Canal Commissioners. Then, Van Buren as leader of the Bucktails would be in a position to control not only the constructing, but the financing of the canal.

Whenever occasion offered, Van Buren asked in his most

---

* Bucktails were originally the Aaron Burr party. When Burr fled after killing Hamilton, his followers changed the name "Aaron Burr Party" to "Bucktails." They identified themselves by a wisp of hair from a deer's tail worn in the hatband.

casual manner the same question of each canal commissioner. What year in the constructing of the canal would be most critical? Most of them believed that if all went well, the construction gangs would be digging the channel across Montezuma Swamp in 1822, and that would be the critical year. Of course it was only a guess, but being the only guess available, Van Buren was forced to base his plans upon it. Since the Constitution of New York State was greatly in need of rewriting to correct various political defects, Van Buren began an undercover agitation for the convening of a New York State Constitutional Convention in 1821. One of the changes Van Buren had in mind was the shifting of state elections from April to November. Another was to limit a governor's term of office to two years instead of three. If these changes were adopted in a new state constitution, Clinton's second term would end on January First, 1823, instead of July First, 1824. Thus if canal construction should go very wrong in Montezuma Swamp in 1822, it might be possible to beat Clinton at the polls in November of that year. As for an opponent, State Supreme Court Justice Joseph Yates, heading the Bucktail ticket, might very well defeat Clinton. Yates was one of the men Van Buren planned to have in his political group.* He knew that he could control Yates.

Also to be changed and controlled was the Council of Appointment, which at that time was under Clinton's control. Van Buren ran over in his mind a few names: Bowne, Moore, Evans, Skinner. With a council like that he could have Thomas Oakley, State Attorney General, discharged and Talcott appointed in his place. Each man and every political maneuver would link and mesh a forward move-

---

* Thurlow Weed in 1830, editor of an Albany newspaper called the *Albany Evening Journal*, gave the name "Albany Regency" to Van Buren's political group.

ment which would roll right over Clinton and perhaps carry Van Buren into the White House.

Meanwhile Clinton, convinced that Van Buren, like any politician, had resolved to become a part of a project which he could not thwart, moved serenely in his orbit making speeches in superb rhetoric to the legislature and to the learned societies, completely unaware that the Red Fox of Kinderhook, far from being impressed, was just a little amused. But neither statesman nor politician could make or break the fate of the Erie Canal. This power lay in the strong hearts and hands of thousands of starving Irishmen who had been harried and dispossessed by misrule and the failure of an agricultural economy which devastated Ireland following the termination of the Napoleonic wars. In 1818 they came to America with the clothes they were wearing, their faith to sustain them, and little else. They built the canal and went on to build American history. Van Buren did triumph temporarily over Clinton, but he never licked the Irish. Neither he nor anyone else.

Before the Irish arrived, the Canal Line had been surveyed from the fork of Tonawanda Creek in Niagara County through virgin forest and across Mountain Ridge, the great stone barrier which holds back Lake Erie from the plains and swamps of central New York ninety feet below.

Two rows of peeled stakes driven forty feet apart marked the width of the water surface of the future canal from tow path to berm, and another row sixty feet further out on each side marked the limits of the Line all the way to Schenectady. The line crossed four very deep ravines before reaching Brockport. It indicated a crossing of the Genesee River at Rochester, crossed Irondequoit Valley southeast of Pittsford, skirted a chain of swamps to Meadville, vanished in the vast Cayuga Marsh, reappeared at Seneca River opposite Montezuma, and edged more swamps to Cossitts* in the Walton Tract a little southeast of Lake Onondaga and its abundant salt springs.

Bearing eastward by northeast, seeking level ground, it passed south of Rome, entered Utica, and ran along the south bank of the Mohawk River to Little Falls, where it met an obstruction, and on to Schoharie Creek where it met another, and so to Schenectady. East of Schenectady the Mohawk passes through a gorge with perpendicular stone cliffs before pitching over Cohoes Falls and streaming through five spouts into the Hudson River. That portion of the line was yet to be surveyed. The projection would require an experienced engineer for solution. At that time there were no men in New York State with sufficient experience or technical education to justify their being called engineers.

Governor DeWitt Clinton had chosen the flat sixteen-mile stretch of wood lots, stump lots, and open pasture between Utica and Rome for the first excavation of the canal channel because its construction would be the only easy portion in the entire line. On the twentieth of November with freeze-up only a few days off, Benjamin Wright, superintendent in charge of building the Erie, and his staff rode horseback along the soft, muddy tow path examining the ditch. It was partly flooded by rain and seepage.

Beside Wright rode Nathan Roberts, a mathematics teacher in the school at Whitestown four miles west of Utica. One side of his school house bordered the canal berm. Behind them rode self-taught, amateur surveyor Canvass White, a narrow-faced, tall Yankee with broad shoulders. As a boy he had been one of Roberts' pupils. Roberts had a precise mouth and a severe, thoughtful expression. White's eyes, rather close together, were brown and steady. Usually a smile lurked at the corners of his mouth. In a

* Syracuse.

coat of hunting pink Wright could have passed for an English country squire. Straggling behind and arguing vociferously were powerful, arrogant David Bates with a hard, calculating eye, who would later be known as the Lock Builder; dark taciturn David Thomas, the surveyor; spry little Marshal Lewis, expert in general construction; and, boss of the stone masons, explosive Welshman Jones ap Kerig.

Two horsemen were riding toward them. White said to Wright, "The one in the gray suit with a gray, low-crowned beaver is Samuel Talcott, our new district attorney in Utica. He graduated from Williams College about eight years ago. The other one looks like Senator Martin Van Buren, leader of the Bucktail Party. Talcott is his staunch supporter. Let's speak to them."

"Hello Talcott. What do you and Attorney General Van Buren think of our canal?"

Talcott spoke, "We have agreed that had you joined the several incisions between Utica and the vicinity of Rome and filled the whole ditch with water, you would have a tolerable waterway for sixteen miles. But if that's all that you can do in a summer, how long will it take you to dig the total three hundred and sixty-four miles?"

Van Buren gave Wright a quizzical look. "Rather amusing, Mr. Wright?"

Wright straightened in his saddle. "Not for us, Mr. Attorney General. We realize that we don't know how to build a canal. We lack the tools, the labor, and we haven't much money but, if we are ever going to be able to defend our Niagara frontier against the British, we must have some way of transporting our military supplies out there. We must find a way to build the canal!"

"Oh come. I was joking. Go with us to a nearby tavern for a few drinks."

White spoke up, "We appreciate your levity, Mr. Attorney General, but we have no time for frivolity. We are desperate. Can you offer us any helpful suggestions?"

Glancing at Van Buren, Talcott gathered his reins. "Only that you abandon a hopeless cause. A dug canal to Lake Erie is obviously impossible. Why not admit it and devote your energies toward improving highways?"

White met Talcott's gleam with glitter. "On my own, I'm leaving tomorrow for New York to catch the last ship for England. I mean to study the workings of the Trent-Mersey Canal. When I return in the spring I'll have some knowledge of canal construction and plenty of sketches. I'll also try to bring back some men who are experienced in canal building."

Van Buren sneered, "If you're thinking of bringing back Englishmen, spare yourself the trouble, young man. We had the foremost British canal engineer, William Weston, working on the Mohawk River for the Lock Navigation Company for several years. An agreeable fellow, but all of the work he did had to be undone, and rebuilt. Being English he could neither adapt his methods of construction to our rough country nor adjust his overbearing ways to our equally rough labor. He had no head for organization. He was extravagant in his expenditures. In the end we had to send him home. Young man, abandon your trip abroad. You'll be wasting your time and money."

White lifted his chin. "Sir, if I had any thought of bringing back Englishmen, I'd agree with you. But you are probably unaware that the English employed some Irish labor in building their canals. Even now a few Irish are employed in canal maintenance. When I return with a gang of Irishmen, such obstacles as I believe you have in mind will disappear like blockades of river ice in the spring."

Talcott said sarcastically, "No need to bring them. Plenty of Irish are currently languishing in New York City jails."

"Sir, I am aware of that. And when I return, I hope to get some of them pardoned and signed up as laborers."

"I can just see you doing it."

White grinned. "Oh I don't know, Governor Clinton is of Irish descent. There is such a thing as a governor's pardon."

Talcott and Van Buren scowled and rode on. Wright frowned at White.

"After I had tried with all my persuasive powers to make you agree with that plan and had failed, along come two enemies of the canal, and, just like that, you speak of my plan as if it were your own."

White grinned back. "You planted the seed in my mind, but far as I know you yourself never did anything about it."

Wright raised his voice, "You know I'm not a procrastinator. If the prisons were filled with Germans or Dutch, I'd have had some of them released so that the canal contractors could hire them. But I had second thoughts when I learned that most of the able-bodied prisoners were Irish. Show me a contractor who could boss a big gang of wild Irish; why, he'd be lucky to get home alive." In a kinder tone Wright continued, "You'll need some money, young man. Will your father provide?"

"Not one dollar! However, I knew from the beginning I'd have to do this on my own. I'll ship before the mast both ways and hire out as a tow-path boy after I arrive. That way I'll see the canals and be paid while doing it."

* * * *

Early the next morning White stopped in Utica at a long unpainted warehouse near Kips Landing beside the backwater of Ballou's Creek at its confluence with the Mohawk River. A lengthy ramshackle dock was littered with the bales, barrels, boxes, baskets, and bundles of bateau freight which bateaumen were loading and discharging as rapidly as space could be found. The bateaux carried bulky freight between Schenectady and Utica in competition with the four-team freight wagons on the Mohawk Turnpike. All of the bateaumen were in a hurry, hoping to make one more round trip before freeze-up compelled them to store their boats and seek winter employment.

The bateaumen were powerful but filthy men who never removed their boots and clothes, not even after falling in the river.

Presiding amid the confusion and keeping it under control, Pippa Post, a girl of twenty-four and owner of the warehouse by inheritance, instructed, agreed to requests or denied them, and scolded and threatened. She wore an ink horn like a pendant. One hand held a quill, the other an accession book. Cowhide short boots, linsey woolsey trousers tucked in at the calf, and a green flannel shirt with sleeves rolled up at the elbows completed her outfit. Her face was round, with cheeks ruddy from out-of-door living, and her long, thick golden hair in a single braid was folded and bound at the back of her neck with a narrow yellow ribbon. She wore neither ornaments nor jewels, but her eyes were of such a brilliant blue that they gave the effect of jewels.

Among those rough, uncouth men she was at ease. Her usually sweet voice was pitched low in a detached business-like tone.

The true reason for her confident manner appeared in the scabbards of two short, heavy knives partially concealed beneath her armpits. While White sat in his saddle watching, a bateauman, shaggy and strong as a black bear, leeringly slipped an arm around her waist crushing her against his deep chest. Faster than White's eyes could follow, two big-bladed knives flashed and struck twice. Wide gashes opened in the man's cheeks, forehead, and chin.

Pippa screamed, "Your eyes and nose next." Before she could strike again, the man had released her and was running for his boat. His face was streaming.

Pippa glared about her. "Anyone else want to try it?" No one spoke or moved.

Slapping the red-stained knives back in their sheaths, she picked up her pen and book and resumed dealings in her normal voice.

From his saddle White broke in with a friendly,

"Good morning Pips, I'm off for England. When I return I may bring you a pair of heavy English skinning knives from Sheffield."

Pippa turned her back on the bateaumen and gave him both of her firm, warm hands.

"When you do, I may have for you a tanned deerskin beaded jacket rubbed with grease until it will shed rain."

At her touch White thrilled, but he could retain her hands for only a moment. The bateaumen clamored for her attention.

"I'll return when the pinksters bloom along the river bank. And I expect to bring some interesting characters with me. Oh, shall I write you?"

"Yes indeed. Tell me of your experiences—and your thoughts. Good-bye, Mr. White."

Pippa withdrew her hands and was instantly surrounded by a knot of insistent bateaumen. White shrugged, heeled his horse, and cantered off.

*   *   *

Twelve weeks later White wrote to Pippa from the Dee Valley in England:

Dear Pippa,

I crossed the bounding main in the forecastle of the City of Bristol. I didn't know a rope from a sail or a tackle block, but by listening to the other sailors and observing, I soon learned. During early winter storms I went with them, sometimes at night, into the toprigging and helped to haul in sails stiff with ice and tie them.

After making port I drew my few shillings of pay and started on foot for the Trent-Mersey Canal. I wanted to see where it ran through a long tunnel.

When night overtook me I stopped at a wayside tavern. They call it a pub. The pub was crowded with rustics drinking beer. I put ten shillings in the hand of the tavern keeper (publican) and shouted that I had placed my money with the publican and would wrestle anyone for two shillings a fall. They looked at me with eyes like shad on a fish counter, but no one spoke. I dropped the stakes to one shilling and four men stood up. I took them on and won. I took two more after that. The publican handed me sixteen shillings and a mug of ale. I declined the ale, but asked for a room.

Just before dawn, in full moonlight, I slid down the thatched roof and went on. I repeated the trick every night until I reached the canal. That day I stopped at noon near a village.

A large sporting crowd, some in coaches, traps, brakes, tallyhos, on horseback and on foot, had gathered round a roped-off ring on the turf. Two men stripped to the waist were fighting with bare knuckles. One wore side burns. He had a flat head, unmistakably English. The other was a sandy-haired Irishman, handsome and very heavily muscled. Muscles of all sizes rippled under his skin. A man beside me whose red coat matched his nose said that the Irishman was J. J. McShane from Temple More, Tipperary, and he was almost licked. He'd been down four times and now was wobbling. While I watched I saw the Englishman throw a haymaker punch which never connected. Yet McShane went down and was dragged with trailing feet by his seconds to his corner. The crowd cheered the Englishman.

McShane was given one minute to recover. Meanwhile a Corinthian in a white hat was shouting odds of six to one against McShane. I offered a hundred shillings (all I had) at

J. J. McShane

eight to one and he covered it. At that price ten Irishmen appeared with a dozen or so of shillings apiece and got their money down.

When time was called McShane tottered from his corner. The Englishman hit him a finishing blow and McShane reeled back against the ropes. The frenzied crowd shouted to the Englishman to go in for the kill. He took their advice, but those ropes acted like a spring which seemed to throw McShane at the Englishman. When they collided McShane hooked the quickest upper cut to the jaw I ever saw. The Englishman went down so hard that he turned over. His seconds dragged him off, but he didn't come back when "time" was called.

I stepped into the ring and hollered, "Hey, you Irish, I can't box, but I'll wrestle you three points on the ground for a fall and two falls out of three for a hundred shillings even."

McShane gave me a surprised look, scowled and nodded. When the crowd learned that I was a Yankee they went wild. Anything to beat the Irish. But, when I had thrown off my jacket and shirt, they could see that he was far stronger than me. So the odds went on McShane. At five to one I again bet every shilling I had.

McShane is strong. When he strikes something has to give, but at wrestling he doesn't know how to make his strength count. Consequently it works against him. As you know, the Mohawk Indians taught me how to wrestle.

I won two falls straight in four minutes. Then the party broke up. I had to run after the man who was holding my clothes, and knock him down to get them. As for my money it had disappeared. Fortunately those ten Irishmen had kept an eye on the stake holder. They caught him as he was getting away. For good measure they gave me what I had bet and all that I had won.

I offered half of my winnings to McShane. He refused, but he did want to know how I had put him down.

We were walking toward a boat tied up on the berm side of the canal. On the bow of the boat, "Shamrock" was painted in green letters. That was his boat. He had been a canal construction engineer. He knew all about building locks, stone-arch aqueducts, embankments, culverts, and how to protect a channel from sliding mud by pounding in sheet piling along the edge, also feeders, waste weirs, and guard locks. He was presently employed with his Tipperary crew as a maintenance man on the Trent-Mersey, the Ellesmere, and the Bridgewater canals. He promised to show me the three gigantic stone arch aqueducts over the Irwell River where boats float one hundred and twenty-seven feet above the ground.

I asked him about Ireland. He replied that nearly all of the food produced in Ireland went to England to pay the rent. The Irish didn't have enough to eat. So he and ten of his friends from Tipperary had come to England where they had found work, but at wages so low that they still didn't have enough to eat. He added that many Irishmen were trying to escape from Ireland, but even if they did he wondered if they would find enough to eat.

I gave it as my opinion that they would, if they came to America and worked on the Erie Canal. When he spoke of passage money, I told him how I had crossed and that I expected to return in the same capacity. McShane discussed it with his men and finally decided to join me as soon as he could sell his boat. He will bring his men, his tools, and drawings.

When we reach New York, McShane wishes to meet Governor Clinton. He will ask the governor to pardon all Irishmen in New York jails on condition that they agree to work for McShane at building the Erie Canal for the duration of their unexpired terms. They will receive standard, prevailing wages, and if promoted, higher wages. If they escape and are caught, they will be returned to prison to serve their terms from the beginning. It's an odd request, but it may bring results. If we don't have a type of labor more resourceful than the Germans and Dutch, the canal will never be built. That's certain.

Of course McShane, if he gets a contract for a section, will require money to finance his work until he has finished enough to warrant inspection and part payment from the state. Pooling our resources we will rent a platform in some large New

York saloon like Martlings and hang out a sign reading, "Ten Men From Tipperary Will Meet all Challengers For Any Stakes—Ten Nights Only."

If some of the patrons prefer to wrestle, that's where I'll enter the show. And if we don't make enough money for the stakes and the betting, we can open for another ten nights in another saloon. As soon as we have enough money to buy food, tents, ploughs, scrapers, draft animals, wagons, wheelbarrows, picks, and shovels for one hundred men, we'll all start for Cossitts in the Walton Tract. There we'll build long bunk houses and a cook shack. The operation will proceed eastward on the canal line south of Oneida Lake across the eastern half of Onondaga County, Madison County, and Oneida County as far as Rome. After I get McShane and his gangs started I'll ride back to Utica to see you. I hope that there won't be any bateaumen around.

> Your humble and obedient
> Canvass

A month after Pippa received that letter, an evil time came for her one evening, as come it must for every beautiful, self-respecting young woman who relies on herself for defense against rough, powerful men who wrestled daily with the river and recognized no control except force.

She had closed and locked her warehouse for the evening, when after a very busy day the boats had either all gone up or down the river, and the water front was deserted. As she was leaving, a bateau slid from the river into the back water and glided to her dock. Two burly, smelly men sprang to the platform and ordered her to unlock so that they could unload.

Pippa tossed her head and walked on. Suddenly from behind she felt an arm was thrown round her neck. Her throat was tightly compressed in a vice-like pinch between a forearm and a bicep. She couldn't even squeak. As she was dragged backward, her key was wrested from the pocket of her breeches. She heard the rattle of the key in the door, the creaking of the hinges. The twilight of the platform gave way to the deep gloom of the interior. While her belt was being unbuckled, a big, dirty hand was clapped over her eyes, probably to keep her from seeing what was about to happen she thought. In a fleeting instant, from the corner of one eye, she saw something slip down from a bale of cotton.

She heard two meaty smacks, two grunts, and she was staggering against a stack of salt barrels. A firm hand steadied her, as an ingratiating voice said,

"Sit down over here on this bale, Miss. I wear brass knuckles on both hands. When I hit 'em they stay hit. I'll be after unloading their boat into the warehouse. I know that they would want it done. After that I'll unload their pockets. Then I'll load them into their boat, push it out into the current and their poles after them. When found it will be assumed that they had a fatal quarrel.

"Here's your belt, Miss. They had started to bind your arms behind you with it when I hit them."

Pippa stood up, rubbing her throat. "I'm very grateful to you. But how did you happen to be in here?"

"I sneaked in an hour ago while you were not looking. I'm just a wanderer by the name of James O'Brien. I always move on the sly so that no one takes notice. It gives me quite an advantage."

Prompted by a strong smell of alcohol Pippa glanced about. Two stone jugs stenciled "H. A." stood on the floor before a wooden case marked "Segars." One jug was out of position. She exclaimed,

"Did you drink that rum?"

O'Brien replied dejectedly, "Yes, but not all of it."

Pippa lifted the jug and set it down. "Most of it. Why that's "Horse Agitator," the brand of rum dishonest sportsmen give their horses just before a race."

O'Brien coughed behind his hand. "Would you sell me the other jug, Miss? Sometimes, when the sheriff's chasing me, that's what I need to help me keep ahead."

Pippa flung the door wide. "The jugs are not mine, but you may take the jug and go. I owe you something for saving my life."

O'Brien picked up a stick with a handkerchief containing his scanty personal effects tied to one end. He ran the other end of the stick through the handle of the jug and ambled to the door. Facing Pippa he asked anxiously,

"Will you be after doing me one last favor, Miss? The sheriff is Apollos Cooper. He's a good man. That he is. But opinionated and somewhat deaf. Not much for listening to reasonable explanations. For slander and libelous accusations he has an open mind. Also he's nosey. He may be looking for me. Just don't sell him what's left in that other jug." O'Brien tipped his broken hat, "Good evening, Miss."

A few weeks later Pippa learned that despite the "Horse Agitator," and a head start, Sheriff Cooper had lodged O'Brien in the Rome jail. At noon while the sun was shining through the barred window of his cell, O'Brien, creating a "burning glass" by filling the crystal of a stolen watch with water, had set fire to the straw in his cell. The fire had spread throughout the jail. Unfortunately the smoke caused the death by suffocation of another prisoner, Elisha Green. O'Brien and two other prisoners, John Harris and David Linus, had been sentenced to imprisonment for three years for grand larceny. Two other prisoners, Denny, a low-browed ape-like man committed for assault with intent, and Pratt, a thin anemic man in for passing counterfeit, were involved.

It had been O'Brien's plan that when the sheriff unlocked and opened the door they would rush out under the cover of smoke and escape. But the opening of the door brought such a rush of air that the whole interior went ablaze. Only by holding a wet towel over his face and crawling on hands and knees did the intrepid sheriff rescue all of the prisoners except Green.

On motion by District Attorney Talcott, the prisoners were tried for causing the death of Green, found guilty by a Talcott-awed jury, and sentenced to be hanged. The prisoners bowed in sullen silence—except Denny. Shaking his manacled fists, his ferocious face livid, he shouted, "Talcott, I'll strangle you for this; if I have to return from the grave!"

Mindful of O'Brien's rescue, Pippa consulted Talcott at the office of Talcott and Maynard in Utica. Believing that Talcott was happily married, Pippa made her appeal impersonal and solely to save the life of O'Brien, whom she thought to be an unfortunate vagrant. Even at that, the interview was inclined to drift away from O'Brien and center upon Talcott's misfortune in having had no reason previously for speaking to Pippa. Ever since coming to Utica he had hoped for an opportunity. Indeed he had first settled in Whitestown, but had removed to Utica so that he could see her more often. Now that she had found the way to his office, Talcott hoped that she would come often. Of course he would take O'Brien's case, and without charge, but his real interest was in Pippa.

Pippa had heard similar appeals from men married and unmarried, but had never been impressed. If Canvass White had made such an appeal, she might have been receptive. But White had never been anything more than friendly. Now under the full impact of Talcott's keen, witty mind and charming personality, she felt her protective instinct weakening. When she demanded an answer about O'Brien's chances, Talcott stated flatly that only a pardon from the governor could save him.

"But how could that be obtained?"

fully. "By knowing the

...s well enough."

...the man had insulted
...yed with herself for not
...ith blue eyes glinting she
...Talcott stood up.

...ng?"

..., Mr. Talcott. O'Brien won't hang."

...other and one of her sisters to take
...ehouse. Then she rented a saddle horse
...n the Seneca Turnpike to Cossitts. Leaving
...at the Walton Tract, she rode northward
...e woods along the edge of the swamps. Distant
...and the crashing of falling trees guided her.

...he had ridden through twilight and moonlight on the
...rnpike, but now the forest was dark. Trees over a hundred
feet high shut out the moonlight. The damp forest floor
was carpeted with a top layer of dry leaves. Pippa tethered
her horse, ripped a cylinder of bark six feet long from a
swamp-edge elm, laid it on a dry spot, stuffed it with dry
leaves, untied the blanket at the back of the saddle,
wrapped it round her, and lay down in the bark cylinder.

At sunrise Pippa rode to the canal line. She smelled
wood smoke, coffee, bacon, and freshly-sawed wood. Standing at the edge of the clearing, she saw that it was about
one hundred and fifty feet wide, over a mile long, and
extended eastward from the edge of the swamp.

A team of oxen hauled a plough which cut furrows from
east to west and back. A sharp blade rigged at the edge
of the plough cut roots up to two inches thick. The plough-
man's handaxe severed thicker roots. Another pair of oxen
dragged a scraper from south to north and back, scraping
the loose dirt to the sides. Hard pan below the loose dirt

was broken up by picks, shoveled into barr
up the sloping sides.

A horseman came cantering up. It was
grinning and very glad to see her. She was ev
see him, but before she could explain her miss
already begun describing to her what the men
after informing her that as a consequence of his
tions in England, he had now been promoted to
tion of Supervisor of Canal Construction.

"Of course, Pippa, these Irish are totally unaccu
to this sort of work. McShane took them from New
prisons, almshouses, even hospitals, and now he's tra
them, aided by ten experienced men whom he brought v
him.

"Way down there you can see that all the trees hav
fallen this way; that is, westward. Because prevailing winds
are from the west, trees in these parts put out their strong
roots on the west side, to hold the trunks against the wind.
There's very little wind from the east, so only a few weak
roots grow on that side of the tree. We anchor our tree
pullers at a safe distance on the west side of the tree, throw
a rope over an upper limb on the east side and, having
made fast, carry the other end back to the puller, wind
it around the shaft, and pull down the tree.

"Axe men chop the branches into short pieces and lay
them crisscross on the ground where the tow path will be.
Then the dirt is thrown on. The pieces of branches function as reenforcement. Strippers remove the bark and mix
it with the dirt layer above the pieces of branches. The
sawyers cut the logs into plank lengths, roll them out of
the way, and stack them.

"You'll notice that the bottom of the canal is not cut
straight down; it's sort of a prism shape, and that's what it's
called—the prism. The very bottom is fourteen feet of flat
earth each way from the center. That's a total of twenty-

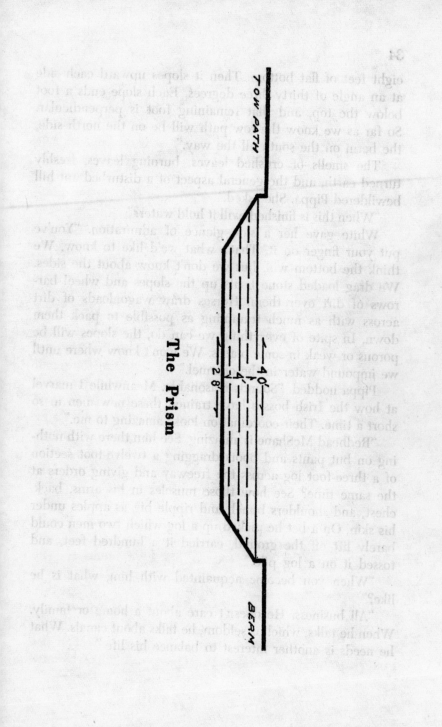

The Prism

eight feet of flat bottom. Then it slopes upward each side at an angle of thirty-three degrees. Each slope ends a foot below the top, and that remaining foot is perpendicular. So far as we know the tow path will be on the north side, the berm on the south all the way."

The smells of crushed leaves, burning leaves, freshly turned earth, and the general aspect of a disturbed ant hill bewildered Pippa. She asked,

"When this is finished, will it hold water?"

White gave her a side glance of admiration. "You've put your finger on it. That's what we'd like to know. We think the bottom will, but we don't know about the sides. We drag loaded stone boats up the slopes and wheel barrows of dirt over them. Horses draw wagonloads of dirt across with as much trampling as possible to pack them down. In spite of everything we can do, the slopes will be porous or weak in some places. We won't know where until we impound water in the channel."

Pippa nodded. "Sounds reasonable. Meanwhile I marvel at how the Irish bosses have trained these new men in so short a time. Their coordination looks amazing to me."

"Redhead McShane is amazing. See him there with nothing on but pants and boots dragging a twelve-foot section of a three-foot log across the freeway and giving orders at the same time? See how those muscles in his arms, back, chest, and shoulders bunch and ripple big as apples under his skin. On a bet he picked up a log which two men could barely lift off the ground, carried it a hundred feet, and tossed it on a log pile."

"When you become acquainted with him, what is he like?"

"All business. He doesn't care about a home or family. When he talks, which is seldom, he talks about canals. What he needs is another interest to balance his life."

"You mean, Mr. White, that he talks about what he sees and hears and not about ideas?"

White nodded. "That's about it, Pippa. And you're a bit that way yourself. Here comes McShane now."

McShane, apparently unaware of Pippa's presence, asked White to ride into Cossitts with a cart and return with a grindstone. The tree trimmers axes had dulled.

White turned to Pippa. "As I introduce J. J. McShane to you, please note that his hair is not dyed. That red fuzz on his chest nearly matches in shade the shock of red hair above. That proves the man is genuine. McShane, meet Miss Pippa Post."

Apparently becoming aware of her presence for the first time, McShane blinked.

"Sure now I've been so occupied with thinking about where I might find someone to keep track of each man's time, figure his pay, inventory the tools and food supplies and order more when needed, and bind up wounds and dispense medicine, not to mention writing a letter to the folks back home in Ireland for men who can't write, that I couldn't see anything beyond my nose. We're busy here getting started."

Pippa's horse moved, bringing her head and shoulders into a small shaft of light. McShane had half turned to go, but he stopped and stared. "Would you be knowing anyone who could answer that description, who would be willing to endure the hardships and work of a construction camp?"

"If it were a woman, would she have a small tent of her own in summer and a log cabin where she could do her paper work in privacy in winter?"

"Aye, that she would."

"Would she receive foreman's pay?"

"Aye, and with a bonus, if she would do all of the things I asked."

"Would I do?"

"You? I was thinking you'd send me an old woman. But you? I dunno, some of these men are rough."

McShane glanced over his shoulder, scowling. All work had stopped. The men had their fingers in their mouths whistling, or were wolf howling, cat-calling, and beckoning. In the foreground two big, hard-faced men whose huge muscles bulged through rents in their shirts were advancing toward Pippa in a meaningful manner. McShane turned back to Pippa. "They haven't seen a young woman in months, and one as comely as you—never in their lives. I'll take care of them now, but as for hiring you, I couldn't stand guard over you and boss this construction at the same time."

Pippa's pink cheeks were flaming, her blue eyes flashing. She slid smoothly from the saddle, her gaze measuring the distance as the men approached. The intent of their outstretched hands was obvious. Pippa murmured to McShane, "Stay where you are and let me handle this."

Turning, McShane spoke sharply, "Mooney! Donohue!" He added something in Gaelic. But on they came, urged by the prolonged uproar behind them, which included obscene suggestions. Mooney and Donohue were only ten paces away when the whole force dropped their tools and started running toward Pippa, streaming in like a folding fan. McShane's face went white. His huge fists doubled. White raised his heavy riding crop. Two men, one mounted, and a woman against so many seemed hopeless, but Pippa stood easy, with body relaxed although her face was hard-set, her eyes calculating.

At their next step Mooney and Donohue had almost converged. That seemed to be what Pippa had been waiting for. She advanced her left foot and swung forward, her hands reaching for the knife handles under each opposite armpit. She swung back, each hand gripping a heavy metal handle and settling back over her shoulders. Then forward with lithe grace, each arm like a catapult sent its missile whizzing and flashing out into the sunshine of the clearing to smack against its target. Mooney and Donohue staggered with eyes and knees crossed and pitched to the ground in a heap. The oncoming workmen stopped, horrified, their attitudes and gestures expressing incredulity. Then, losing interest, they turned and hurried back to their work.

White spoke quickly. "They're all right, McShane. She brought 'em down with the hafts. With the blades she'd have killed them. They'll come to in a minute, sort themselves out, and return to work with headaches."

White dismounted, retrieved the knives, and gave them to Pippa, who had already resumed her saddle. McShane, stupefied, glanced alternately at Mooney and Donohue crawling and trying to rise and at Pippa's full, curved lips. Throwing up his dirt-stained hands McShane shouted,

"Saints preserve us, I never saw anything like it. And a woman at that. What must the men hereabouts be like?"

White interrupted. "Listen McShane, you are working on an American frontier. You can't change it. So you might just as well get used to it."

Pippa chuckled sweetly. "Mr. McShane, this place fascinates me. Do I get the job of bookkeeping?"

"Bookkeeping? You? No. I'm hiring you to follow me around and protect me from the Indians and the wolves and bears and tigers. After what I've seen I don't feel safe at all."

In an aside White spoke to Pippa. "Do you really wish to work here?"

"Oh yes. A hundred rough men. And I'll be the only woman."

"You may not be."

"I'll see to that. Canvass, I came because you wrote in your letter that you'd be here. I couldn't wait until you came to Utica. You see, a vagrant named James O'Brien saved my life, and he's now in Rome jail under death sentence. If you could get him a commutation of sentence, the governor might pardon him for canal work."

White muttered, "O'Brien? O'Brien. Oh Yes! He's a pickpocket and thief, always in trouble, but resourceful. From what McShane says, he needs a right-hand man as well as a clerk. Under McShane O'Brien might develop into a smart, capable superintendent. I'll speak to McShane, then see the governor. In six weeks O'Brien will be free."

Pippa thanked him with her eyes. She said, "I must now return to Utica, find someone to take my place at the warehouse—then I'll roll my tent and pack my baskets. I'll put my pack baskets on my donkey, and he'll follow my horse."

Three hours later Pippa and White were riding eastward on the Seneca Turnpike toward Utica, but still in Onondaga County. On their right rose the crumbling limestone cliffs of Sullivan. They had guided their horses through an eighth of a mile of sheep and a quarter of a mile of pigs being driven to Albany market. The pigs were tired and wished to rest. The sheep behind them were nervous because the pigs wouldn't let them through. Their respective drovers and dogs took a dim view of each other. Through the dust, smell, bleating, grunting, barking, and cursing White created a path. Pippa followed.

It was a distressing kind of experience. Five miles beyond they encountered another type. Ahead of them a middle-aged man with a knapsack was tossing in air what appeared to be a ball of mud and catching it as he pranced along singing.

A tisket, a tasket, a green and yellow basket
I made a ball of limestone
And in a pail I dropped it.

He allowed the ball to land on a flat rock in the road. It bounced nearly two feet.

Pippa exclaimed, "That's the first time I ever saw a mud ball bounce."

White shouted, "Hi, Andrew Bartow! Let me see that ball."

Stammering with excitement Bartow turned back and gave it to him. White weighed it in his hand.

"Is that Roman cement?"

"Sure is. And it came from those cliffs up there. There's a farmer around here named Sullivan. He said that his soil was wet and acid. To sweeten it he ground up some of this limestone and spread it. But it didn't sweeten. It just became hard in the wet soil. That made me curious. I rented a blacksmith shop last Sunday, pounded up a lot of the stone on an anvil, and burned it to powder in the forge. Two English masons, brothers named Horn, helped me. They are employed on the canal. In England they worked on the Duke of Bridgewater's canal and were familiar with the type of limestone used over there for making Roman cement. They call it meager limestone because it's so crumbly that it can't be used for building.

"Anyway, I wet the powder after mixing it with sand and made a ball of it. I dropped the ball into a pail of water and let it stand overnight. In the morning it was like this. Now I'm taking some of the stone home in my knapsack so that I can get Professor James Hadley of Fairfield Medical College to make some experiments.

"Within a week I'll have perfected a formula for making hydraulic cement. Then we can build stone aqueducts, stone-arched bridges, and stone locks. Construction of the canal will require many thousands of bushels of cement, but to buy it in England would be too great an expense for the state to bear. Thanks to me we don't have to buy it. We can make it ourselves. Right up there on those cliffs there's more meager limestone than we can possibly use. Engineer White, the canal now becomes a reality."

White reached down and grasped Bartow's hand. "Here, jump up and ride behind me. You must be in Fairfield by tomorrow. The canal can't wait."

Pippa gave Bartow a scathing look. Just when she was sure of having all of White's attention for a good long ride, unhampered by either sheep or pigs, Bartow had to appear.

Seeming to have forgotten her, White urged his horse to a canter. Pippa held her horse back, letting White ride out of her life, telling herself that she liked Talcott better anyway. Besides, there was McShane and all of his Irish. And furthermore, if White's horse should break in the middle from the overload and drop them into a puddle, she'd pass at a trot and leave them walking, carrying the saddle. Maybe the pigs would overtake them. She hardened her heart, tossed her head, and set her face toward Utica. When an attractive man had to choose between a young woman and the canal—the canal won every time. Men!

Chapter 2

BECAUSE PIPPA was interested in all men, deeply interested in three men, and not at all interested in any one man to the exclusion of other men, she easily made a place for herself in McShane's camp. As soon as the men had become accustomed to seeing her around and had adjusted to the condition that although beautiful as a ripe apple she was nevertheless forbidden fruit, they gave her only passing attention. They found their favorite pastimes of singing, drinking, fighting, and playing cards for money more diverting than trying to climb a glass mountain to reach a princess.

Pippa ate her evening meal at one end of the long, rough-hewn plank table. McShane sat at the other. That was about as close to him as she could get. The men who sat near her were courteous, but restrained. Whisky jugs circulated freely, and there was plenty of singing, but no shady remarks or off-color stories, and no profanity. Pippa perceived that their restraint was due mainly to the sharp eye that McShane kept upon them. As there was no relaxing of his vigilance, and no one came near her tent, not even McShane, Pippa concluded rightly that McShane stood inflexibly for the sanctity of respectable womanhood.

When the quality of the cooking deteriorated beyond excuse, Pippa asked, and was granted, permission to take over. She demonstrated the art, then stood back and watched the cooks until they had cooked the food properly. Afterward she supervised the washing of dishes and utensils.

Next morning, happily aware of the many approving glances, she asked McShane's permission to select a camp site to be used the following night, for she had ranged the forest most of her life and knew how to pitch a comfortable camp. Reluctantly McShane assigned two men furnished with peavy, saw, axes, and shovels to assist her—reluctantly, because he really couldn't spare them.

Pippa picked up a hatchet and a coil of rope and, followed by the two men with a tree puller and her horse and donkey, walked along bermside looking for a dry stretch slightly elevated. She found it a mile beyond the face of falling trees where the gangs were working. By careful selection they found and dropped a hemlock, which caromed off other trees without becoming lodged and finally fell to the ground. While the men slashed the branches and trimmed them, Pippa peeled the bark in great slabs and rolls. Then she ordered them to pull down another hemlock, to fall as nearly parallel as possible to the one on the ground, which when cleared of branches and bark would be rolled so close to the other that there would be only four feet between them. In that space she laid enough of the bark to cover the ground. She then spread a thick mat of hemlock tips on the bark. The trimmed branches were laid across the tops of the logs and made strong supports for a roof of bark slabs. The roof was not completely watertight, but then neither was the bark roof of a bunk house. Unless it rained heavily at night, the men, rolled in their blankets, would sleep warm and dry.

Enough more trees were pulled down, and similarly treated, to house the whole work force. Pippa continued the clearing until she had spread a bark carpet on the ground with a low, peaked bark roof over it where the men could eat while it was raining. She dug an earthen fireplace with a clay oven for the cooks. In the remaining shreds of daylight, she rigged a sort of shelter for her horse and the draft animals.

During the day the tree pullers had approached within

half a mile. They were closer to her new camp than the bunk house they had made. When McShane came through and saw what she had prepared, including a blazing cooking fire, he ordered all of his men to gather their baggage and move up. Pippa helped the cooks to assemble a meal, ate a few scraps, then guided her donkey back to her tent. She had a tarpaulin rigged behind the tent to protect him.

That night it rained until the forest floor was soaked, but cleared toward morning. The men had slept soundly and in a dry state. After breakfast they were ready and eager for work, and the wet earth made tree pulling easier.

After looking over the camp McShane came to a decision. When Pippa appeared, he extended his right hand and said, "The first time I saw you I said to myself, 'Another girl. And women are the devil for stirring up trouble, especially the comely ones.' So I began to think of how I could get rid of you. Lucky for me the answer to that question never came. I had another question nagging me. How could I build camps without delaying progress, as we worked along? Sure the men can't work in the rain all day and lie down on the ground and be rained on all night.

"As matters stood we couldn't dig the channel to meet the contractors digging westward from Rome before freeze-up. If we failed, we'd be so far behind schedule that we couldn't possibly reach Seneca River before November of next year. And besides digging the channel we must erect aqueducts this fall across Oneida, Canaseraga, and Chittenango creeks. Until last night I hadn't slept, but thanks to you. . . . Take your donkey and go up the line a mile and build another camp like this one."

Pippa ignored McShane's proffered hand. Tossing her head she said, "Dig the channel and build the aqueducts. Still your men must have food and a dry place to sleep. That's my province."

McShane hastily withdrew his hand. "Sure it will be

your province to find us a dry place for sleeping. But as for food, out in the woods we have learned to care for ourselves."

"Is that so? Then how do you account for the fact that tree after tree comes down with porcupines, racoons, and an occasional one with wild honey, all of which can be cooked with wild roots into an abundant and delicious stew. And yet your men go hungry because commissary wagons are slow in arriving. You don't know how to live off the land. You have me to teach you, and you do nothing about it."

McShane shrugged. "It looks as if I'm to have a partner whether or no. Go ahead and make the camps and boil the porcupines, if it makes you happier. Adam couldn't win an argument with Eve. Nor has any man since.—Oh Shamus, when you're trimming off branches, don't cut so close to your foot!"

Next day Shamus did cut his foot. Summoned to attend, Pippa, while preparing bandages, informed him that he must keep off his feet for at least two weeks. In his pale Irish face there was no expression as he asked tonelessly, "And if I don't?"

"You'll bleed to death because there is no way to keep the wound closed."

"No way at all?"

"Except by dripping flame-melted pitch on the gaping wound. The pain is unendurable."

"Do you know how to do it?"

"I've watched the Indians do it. They gather pine sap on the end of a stick until they have a ball the size of a butternut. They set fire to the ball and drip the melted pitch into the wound. That cauterizes and seals it. But no one except an Indian can endure the pain."

"Know where to get the pine sap?"

"Sure."

"Get it. And hurry. My gang's two trees behind already."

After Pippa had administered the treatment, bandaged his foot, and watched him hobble off to his gang, she murmured, "The Indians and the Irish. And the torture stake. They'll endure anything to show off."

* * * *

The construction of shelters in advance of the work force kept Pippa occupied. Between times, and usually in her tent by candle light at night, she entered in her account book a record of McShane's supplies of food and spare tools. When replenishment was indicated she secured a written order from him to Mr. John Devereux in Utica, rode a few miles southward through the forest to the Seneca Turnpike and gave it with two shillings to anyone traveling eastward. Then she rode back. Within five days the supplies would be brought in by wagon on an abandoned logging road from Seneca Turnpike down Canaseraga Creek to the canal line.

Canaseraga Creek was low. Standing in the middle of its gravel bed, five feet upstream from what would be the north side of the tow path, McShane probed with an iron bar. A few feet down he struck hard pan. Summoning his pick and shovel men, he ordered an excavation ten feet square down to the hard pan. Ten hewn timbers each ten feet long and one foot square would be laid in the excavation. Upon them ten more would be laid crisscross. Holes were to be bored and iron rods inserted to bind the timbers together. Planks sawed four-inches thick would be laid over the upper layer of timbers, again crisscross and spiked down. The squared timbers were called "sleepers," and the completed layers were known as a "mat."

McShane ordered an excavation made in each bank, starting at the north side of the tow path line to a width of ten feet extending in an upstream direction for twenty-seven feet. The bottom of each excavation had to be of

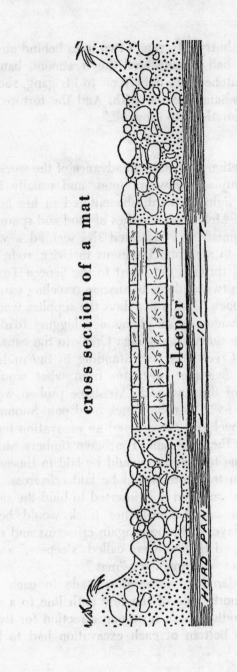

cross section of a mat

the same depth as the excavation in the middle of the creek bed. By using a transit theodolite and red-and-white-banded surveying rod, they were able to dig the bottoms of the three excavations to almost exactly the same level.

Meanwhile the axe men had been preparing sleepers for all three excavations. Carpenters, self-taught, dug a saw-pit and sawed out the planks together with some two-inch planks to be used in building forms for two twenty-foot arches. McShane dispatched Pippa on her horse to the stone quarry at Split Rock, on a hill south of Cossitts, with an order for enough stone blocks to build two arches, each with a twenty-foot span, eight feet high and ten feet wide. He specified in the order that after the blocks had been chiseled at the quarry, they must be laid on the ground and built up in a concavity like a sentry box to be sure that each stone fitted, allowing for quarter-inch interstices between blocks so that there would be room for cement. And speaking of cement, she was to find Bartow's cement works near Sullivan and ask how much longer his customers must wait for delivery.

As she received the order Pippa asked, "Aren't you forgetting Chittenango Creek? We left it behind some time ago. It's nearly three times as wide as this one."

McShane smiled grimly. "Sure Colleen, I wish I could. But I can't build an aqueduct without cement. I'm giving the lads some practice with this small creek before I tackle a bigger one."

Pippa persisted. "How will you build the canal across streams smaller than this one?"

"We'll be pulling away the stones in the stream bed until we've made a smooth gravel bed some sixty-feet long. On the bed we'll lay lengths of two-foot-wide iron pipe and lock them together into one continuous length. Then we'll make an embankment on which the canal channel will cross above the stream and lay a stone apron on the slope of the embankment at either end of the pipe to hold the earth until weeds and bushes can become established. The stream will pass through the pipe. The diameter of the pipe we'll select will vary with the volume of water in the stream."

"But how can you hold water in a channel dug across the loose dirt of an embankment?"

"We line that part of the channel with blue clay to a depth of three or four inches. That holds the water in. It's called puddling. Now be off with you."

McShane slapped the horse's rump so hard that the horse kicked back at him. As the horse galloped westward on the smooth channel bottom, Pippa calculated the number of hours she could be away before the food supplies arrived. She must return in time to check them. The corners of her lovely lips curved in a hard little smile. Now she had become a part of the McShane organization.

Leaving the canal line at Chittenango Creek she crossed to Seneca Turnpike. After inquiring, she found Bartow's lime kiln at Sullivan, and Bartow puttering about trying to improve the quality of his product. From his responses and hang-dog manner, she surmised that he was hen-pecked and had become accustomed to that condition of life. On impulse she gave him the sort of tongue lashing she had heard her mother administer her father when he had lost all of his wealth during a conflagration in Utica. Bartow shook his large ears and went to work. Pippa followed him, nagging and abusing him until his ears turned pink. She stepped up her abuse in shrill tones until his ears were flaming and he wouldn't look at her. Those were the symptoms she remembered. Confident that a delivery of cement would reach McShane's camp before she could return, she rode toward Split Rock.

The stone cutters, smoking clay pipes, were chipping at rock as if carving sculptures rather than blocks. They were in no hurry. Acting on another impulse, Pippa waved an old food supply list at them and demanded, "Do you scarecrows know what this is?"

Astonished, they shook their heads.

"I'm a process server, and this is a dispossess notice from Albany. Read it."

While they passed it around, studying it upside down and sideways, Pippa held her breath. With questioning looks they returned the paper. As she had hoped, none of them could read. In a haughty tone she gave them an order, "The Canal Commissioners in Albany must have stone blocks of standard size for two twenty-foot arches at Canaseraga Creek and for four more arches at Chittenango Creek. They can't wait until next year. They must build them now. If you don't cut those blocks, the state will commandeer this quarry, and you can't have it back until the state's needs have been filled. You'll be out of work. What will your wives say?"

They looked at each other askance. They all had grizzled chins; some stained with tobacco, and others just stained. One propounded, "My name is Martin Vrooman. How many perch of stone will that be?"

Pippa snapped back, "For both aqueducts, an estimated three hundred and twenty-five cords."

"How much do you pay a cord?"

"Four dollars and a half a cord delivered."

"You've bought 'em. Come on boys, start loading the wagon while I hitch the horses. Y'see now I was right? 'bout cutting a few hundred cord to have some on hand? You predicted we couldn't get three fifty a cord."

Pippa returned to McShane chagrined at having paid a dollar per cord too much. Because the blocks had been expertly cut, McShane said nothing until all of the stone had been delivered. His men had piled the blocks in cords eight by four by four. However, Vrooman insisted that a

single row eight-feet long and four-feet high was a cord.
After a futile protest Vrooman accepted McShane's meas-
urement of a cord, his money, and drove away.

Through their natural skill and eagerness to discover
and adopt more efficient ways of doing things, the fabulous
Irish had built the forms for the arches at Canaseraga
Creek before the barrels of cement and stone blocks had
arrived. Meanwhile, by walking with torches all night, the
pick and shovel men had returned to Chittenango. Without any rest they began digging big holes in the creek bed
to contain the mats.

Pippa followed on horseback leading her donkey. The
pack baskets slung across the donkey's back contained jugs
of whiskey, tea, and bread. As soon as the tea had boiled
she poured in whiskey, decanted it into cups, sliced the
bread, and served. After a bite and a gulp the men worked
as if refreshed by a night's sleep. By noon the grub wagon
had arrived. Pippa had lit cooking fires up-wind of the men.
The savory steam of bubbling pork and lamb stew renewed
their energy.

Pippa watched the men dig a trench four-feet wide
straight upstream for a distance of twenty-five feet, beginning where the bases of the two central arches came
together. Crisscross sleepers were inserted, fastened with
rods, planked, spiked, and overlaid with grouting. Cement
had already arrived. More stone blocks were on the way.
A thick coating of concrete had barely hardened when the
masons were laying a four-foot-wide stone wall extending
upstream on the grouting base. Concomitantly the carpenters were erecting wooden forms for the arches. Having
finished the stone wall, the masons erected, at the upstream
end, a stone spire as high as the tow path.

Deep niches were cut in opposite banks twenty-three
feet long and built up with stone blocks and cement to a
level one foot lower than canal bottom. The carpenters had

been busy squaring logs into one-foot timbers fifty-five feet long. The timbers were laid from the niche in the bank to the twenty-five-foot-long stone pier projecting upstream and spiked together. That formed the floor of a trough. The sides were built up until they were level with the tow path crossing on arches which had been only partially completed.

As soon as they had finished their work, the men left in pairs and threes hurrying back to the face of excavation moving daily eastward. Pippa followed.

Before reaching Oneida Castle the canal line bent north-eastward, keeping to the level ground and avoiding the hills. After digging a few miles in that direction, the men reached Oneida Creek. The ravine was one hundred and twenty feet wide. The engineers' plans called for an all-stone aqueduct. The piers would have to be thirty feet long, extending upstream, and four feet wide. The arches would have a twenty-foot span and a width of thirty feet. A four-foot parapet along each side would hold the water in on the south and function as a guard rail on the north.

This all-stone construction required not only strong, sound bases for all of the piers and abutments, but a perfect fit for every stone block and a binding seal of cement between blocks. Canvass White, having kept an eye on McShane's phenomenal progress, had already summoned David Bates and Marshall Lewis to come with their stone cutters, masons, stone boats, and oxen.

The crumbly limestone in the long range of cliffs south of Chittenango and Canastota was of the best variety for producing cement, but was of little value for outdoor construction. The Split Rock quarry was now too distant. White rode southward from Oneida Castle on the Oneida Trail for eight miles. Then he rode up the southeastern slope of Stockbridge Hill. At one thousand feet of elevation he found an outcropping of excellent building stone. He blazed a path

slanting northeasterly down the hill to the trail and rode
to McShane's camp to enlist some tree pullers and sawyers
to construct a stone boat trail on the line of his blaze.

Ireland, a gently rolling country, had given McShane's
men no experience in building roads for heavy loads on
steep hillsides. Sketching diagrams in mud with a stick,
Canvass White explained as best he could about steep
grades, thick chains dragged as brakes beneath the stone
boats, and long ropes looped around snubbing posts for
lowering a loaded stone boat down a sharp slope.

Two horse-drawn carts were loaded with food, blankets,
a stone boat, ropes, and tools. Ten men started in the afternoon. By nightfall they had found the blazed trail, left two
men at the foot to make camp and care for the horses, and
gone up to the outcropping which marked the site of the
quarry. By lanthorn light they removed enough earth to
reveal the seams in the rock. With drill, feather wedge, and
sledge they opened a cavity in the ledge and set aside several large chunks.

They built a fire, dozed until dawn, then broke off more
rock. To begin, they rolled rocks down the hill to the
Oneida Trail. There they erected a log bunker to stop the
rolling stones, which trees on the hillside had braked in
their descent. The two men at the bottom chiseled the
stones into squares, loaded them on the stone boat, hitched
the two horses to it, and set off for the canal line crossing
of Oneida Creek. Four hours later they had delivered their
load and started back. They made another round trip that
day. The next day two more stone boats joined them.

Pippa rode into Utica, loaded two kegs containing
twenty-five pounds of musket powder in each of two pack
baskets on the donkey and, riding west on the Seneca Turnpike, turned south on Oneida Trail and delivered the
powder for blasting rock. Indians from Oneida Castle
appeared with horses and stone boats. McShane appointed

John Clancy to coordinate the operation. Already men had been sent ahead of the channel diggers to excavate for the foundations of piers and abutments in the bed of Oneida Creek.

The quiet of that wilderness glade was disturbed when the channel men were still a mile away. It was shattered when the foundation men got to work, and it became noisier as more and more stone boats were arriving. Then the channel men came amid the roar and crash of falling trees. Cement wagons followed. The crossing became pandemonium. Work went on all night by torchlight, and well it did, for autumn rains were causing the creek to rise. Through the seeming confusion McShane moved constantly, directing by shouts and gestures; McShane, the man who had no time for sleep.

The aqueduct was created in the wilderness out of wilderness materials within a few days. Oneida Creek was dammed. A feeder ditch with guard gate and corresponding waste weir were added. Gradually the uproar subsided. The quarry was abandoned. The whole noisy, smoky operation moved northeastward. With the restoration of quiet, two deer came to the creek to drink and gaze wonderingly at the strange new aqueduct which the shouting, cursing men had left behind. Suddenly the deer pricked up their ears. Above the distant crash and rumble came the harmony of many Irish voices singing. Never before had the deer heard anything like that.

* * * *

Yet to be constructed were ten stone arches, each spanning a fair-sized brook, and three embankments to fill three deep ravines drained by small streams. In each embankment a round iron culvert two or three feet in diameter and seventy-six feet long would suffice to carry even a freshet through the embankment. To finish the work four feeder dams and waste weirs would also be constructed.

The weather alternated, with the warm spells progressively less warm and each cold period colder than the preceding. As the temperature of the soil approached freezing, the men sleeping on the ground lost heat from their bodies faster than they could replace it. This speeded up their circulation and kept them awake. They tired easily.

They were six miles from Rome and progressing slowly when Pippa returned from a scout and reported that the contractors working westward to meet them were less than a mile away. The men cheered, spit on their hands, and were about to double their effort when Pippa held up a hand and called to McShane.

"I rode close enough to hear them talking. They know where we are. Tonight they are coming here to attack us while we are asleep. Their plan is to chase us out of here, take our tools and animals, burn everything they can't use, and then claim that they have done most of the work we have done and demand to be paid for it. I think that many of those men have been hired and put there by the Regency."

An animal growl greeted her words. McShane shouted, "Silence! 'Tis not the likes of you that's giving the orders. You'll do as I say, or I'll be knowing the reason why. Stop all work. Hitch horses to carts and oxen to stone boats. Load all ploughs, scrapers, pullers, and tools on the vehicles. Roll and tie your blankets and shoulder them. Carry the kettles, tableware, and food in your wheelbarrows and start for our bunk house at the edge of Caldwell's swamp. And walk day and night and don't stop for anything until you get there.

"Stone cutters! Unstrap your hammers and chisels and cut in that boulder over there—'McShane—November 28, 1819.'

"Miss, ride back with your donkey and all your baggage and tell those bullies of the Regency that in the dusk the Irish will be streaming through the forest to attack them front and flanks and they'd be smart to erect a barricade to make us attack at a disadvantage. Give them to understand that we've driven you out. We are hard, desperate men. And you have had enough of us. Then ride on home. We hope to see you again in the spring."

John Clancy called, "McShane, is it to run away from a fight you are asking us?"

From the sky came a gabbling sound as of many people shouting and cheering. McShane pointed. "Not from a fight, Clancy, but a storm. The sky is black with geese and they're heading south. There's a storm behind 'em. If we don't reach shelter in twenty-four hours, we'll never fight anyone."

For over an hour there was a hurry and bustle in the canal line which matched the ominous portent above. Without bidding good-bye Pippa rode away to do her part in detaining the roughs of the Regency. She must make her story convincing. Those uncouth men were suspicious by nature and would be hard to convince.

McShane, the last to leave the face of work, paused to admire the words cut in the rock. Yielding to impulse he picked up a stick and scratched in the sloping bank of the prism, "April Fool," added a sketch of a boy wearing a pointed dunce cap, broke the stick across his knee, and followed his men.

It was thirty-six miles to the bunk house. McShane, the last to arrive, reached it as it was growing dark the following day. By that time it was snowing hard and the north wind was rising.

Chapter 3

EACH YEAR, during the period of canal construction, the state legislature voted an appropriation for canal expenses. Throughout the administration of DeWitt Clinton the canal appropriation held priority on the legislative calendar, but the appropriation was never large. Although economy was rigidly enforced, and in most cases faithfully observed, the expenses were many, occasionally very large and quite unforeseen. By December First the money had been spent, and the succeeding sixty days were more or less a waiting period pending the next appropriation.

The contractors working southwest from Rome probably would have pushed through the last mile of timber, found McShane's name chiselled on that boulder, and chiselled it out but for the sudden arrival of the snow storm. After the storm the first to traverse that part of the canal line were Ben Wright, head boss of the western division, and his assistant, Canvass White. They saw the inscription and, as they rode on, the fine work which McShane had done. Later they cautioned the other contractors about the stone. It was not to be defaced. McShane received credit for his work and the promise of pay when it was available. Meanwhile McShane had to buy winter clothing and new leather boots for his men, as well as food, warm blankets, and whiskey. Another expense was hay for his horses and oxen. It all descended upon him. It was his responsibility, and he had in his pockets only five hundred dollars.

When the snow had stopped and the following wind which rearranged it had quieted, McShane trudged over to the Seneca Turnpike. He was followed by Mooney, Donohue, and Clancy.

The Seneca Turnpike crossed Caldwell's Swamp and the rest of the Walton Tract on a wide corduroy road, slippery because it lay in a swamp and was always wet. It's east-west course was south of the canal line. Diverging from the turnpike about half-way across, a narrow corduroy, functioning as a private road, led to a small clearing in the swamp where Judge Joshua Forman had that summer built and occupied a two-story frame house. About half-way between Forman's and Onondaga Creek a north-south road of sorts crossed the turnpike, creating a "Four Corners" which had been known as Bogardus or Cossitts according to the name of the current proprietor of the wretched tavern at the crossroads. Judge Forman, impelled by the Greek Revival, had renamed the Four Corners—Corinth. A red grist mill had been set up where Onondaga Creek was barred with a log dam. There was also a school house and, scattered about the marsh, log huts and shanties inhabited by people who must have liked swamp life and fauna.

McShane strode up to Judge Forman's door and knocked. As soon as he gave his name, Judge Forman welcomed him. McShane described his financial problem frankly, then asked the judge if there were any wealthy men in the salt industry now developing on the southwestern shore of Lake Onondaga. Forman replied that Freeman Hughes had paid cash for the salt business owned by James Geddes the founder. Since then several independents had started boiling the salt water which flowed in abundance from the many salt springs. Because of McShane's reputation Forman thought it likely that Geddes would be quite willing to help him. However Geddes had been given charge of building the Champlain Canal and was therefore presently unavailable. As for the independents, they had some money although none were wealthy.

McShane described casually the plan which he, the Tipperary Ten, and Canvass White had used in New York

JAMES GEDDES

to raise money, the gate, side bets, the purse, and the rare instances when they failed to win a fight. McShane attributed their success to the Irish trait of thoroughly enjoying a fight, whereas men of other nationalities fought to prove to their friends, and themselves, that they were not afraid to fight.

Forman, a graduate of Union College where fights between students and citizens were a daily occurrence, understood at once. He said that King Allen, Nate Whitney, and George O'Neill were leaders among the Salt Boilers, who, by the way, were mostly Irish or of Irish extraction. Freeman Hughes had money, disliked Irish, and would bet against Irish strangers. The men best qualified to stir up Hughes were the brothers Shanahan—John, James, and Ed. If McShane and his men were to appear at ringside, boasting (with a little play-acting to make the boast convincing) that they could lick any Salt Boiler with one hand tied behind them, they could secure long odds in their side bets against Salt Boiler boxers.

McShane interrupted, "Sure there'll be no need for play acting. We're that exhausted from overwork that the four of us together could hardly lick a boy."

Forman paused, "Then why do you risk your money?"

McShane shook his head. "'Tis all the money I have. The lads have none. Mr. Forman, 'tis no matter how weary and lame we may be. To eat we must win, trusting in what is called the luck of the Irish."

Forman dispatched his clerk, John Wilkinson*, to find the Shanahans and send them out to the Salt Works to get the audience together, shovel snow, pound stakes into the half-frozen ground, and string ropes to mark the twenty-four foot ring.

By the time McShane and his three fighting men had

---

* He gave Syracuse its name.

arrived, a big bell was ringing and the Salt Works had been closed. Such a boisterous, pugnacious crowd had assembled that the Shanahans had found it expedient to provide a dozen men with horse whips and appoint them as whippers to hold the crowd in check, twenty feet back from the ring. Any unauthorized person entering that open space was whipped unmercifully.

While McShane was stripping to the waist Wilkinson announced from the ring that they were about to enjoy the privilege of seeing the strongest man in the world, the great McShane of Temple More, Ireland, who had fought a draw in the London Prize Ring with Tom Cribb, and another with Molyneaux. He had been persuaded to stop at the Salt Works to meet any challenger in a finish fight for a purse of five hundred dollars, winner take all. In response, Dean Richmond, Charles Woodruff, and Tobias Buckley had each placed with Judge Forman five hundred dollars in cash. The McShane had offered to cover bets for any amount at two to one against himself. The Shanahans sat at an improvised desk, had the book, and were holding the money.

As individuals the Salt Boilers had, at various times, collided with Richmond, Woodruff, and Buckley. They knew the feel of their fists, and they had lost money in dealing with them. That their champions were risking their own money was all that they needed to know. Waving bank notes and bags of silver coins they surged toward the Shanahans.

When Judge Forman, acting as McShane's backer and banker, had covered all bets, Mr. Victory Birdseye of Pompey, a nearby village, climbed through the ropes and declaimed that the rules would be London Prize Ring, a stand-off fight in each instance. Any contestant who attempted rough and tumble tactics would be declared loser. He called McShane and Richmond into the ring, introduced them, sent them to their corners, and told them at the call of "time" to come out fighting.

At the outset neither McShane nor any of his opponents made any attempt at defense. Indeed they seemed to court punishment as a stimulant to anger and the delivering of harder blows. For a few rounds there was only the smell of blood and sweat and sounds like chopping meat with a cleaver, followed by howls from the spectators, as if in sympathetic pain. As red blotches appeared on the contestants' bodies, they began instinctively guarding against oncoming blows. This was the moment for which McShane had been waiting. He sent a straight left to Richmond's head. When his opponent raised his arms to ward off the blow, leaving his stomach exposed, McShane gave him a solar plexus punch which doubled him forward. A hard uppercut to the chin snapped back his opponent's head. Before executing the final punch McShane maneuvered Richmond into a position where, as he fell backward, he would whack his head against a corner stake. But the stake collapsed under Richmond's weight. Fighting was suspended while, amid groans and boos from the spectators, the stake was hastily replaced.

A round ended whenever a contestant fell. His seconds immediately dragged him to his corner and applied restoratives. One minute later, if he was unable to appear in the ring and continue to fight, he was declared a loser. As one round had succeeded another it had seemed to McShane that within his considerable ring experience he had never fought such a durable man. Although he repeatedly hit Richmond so hard that when he struck the ground he turned over, he was always on his feet again at the call of "time." As a last resort McShane induced contact between the vulnerable back of Richmond's head and a stronger looking stake. That stake like the others had been driven hurriedly into partially frozen ground, but it held when

Richmond struck it; thereby improving McShane's finances by several hundred dollars.

While Mooney and Donohue were removing their shirts McShane put his on, walked over to the table piled high with bank notes and silver, and spoke in a low tone to the Shanahans. They nodded to Birdseye. He stepped into the ring and announced that McShane was offering to bet even money all of the cash on that table that Mooney and Donohue would knock out Buckley and Woodruff.

A forward surge of Salt Boilers who had not lost all of their money on Richmond kept all three of the Shanahans occupied until silver and bank notes were stacked even higher on the table. McShane, from blackened eyes above swollen, bleeding cheeks, gave Mooney and Donohue a hard look as they were stooping to pass through the ropes. They nodded assurance that there would be no failure.

Mr. Birdseye was already in the ring proclaiming that for the first time in prize ring history two champions would fight two other champions; two Irishmen against two Americans. Because of arduous labor in digging the canal the Irish were too tired to fight. But they were game. Despite this inducement no one would bet against the Irish unless given odds of two to one. While last-minute bets were being recorded, Birdseye scuttled out of the ring and the great Salt Works fight began.

Under cover of the uproarious response of the crowd to the first exchange of blows, Clancy swept the money from the table into a large canvas bag. Meanwhile, with his right fist Mooney broke through Buckley's guard and doubled him. His left sent Woodruff staggering. Donohue slipped around behind them, gave one a rabbit punch across the back of his neck and the other a kidney punch in the small of his back. When both Salt Boilers turned on Donohue, Mooney administered the rabbit and kidney punches in reverse order. As they were turning back to Mooney, Donohue delivered upper cuts. Mooney jarred the breath out of them with solar plexus blows. Under a storm of punches Woodruff and Buckley sank to the ground like two schooners foundering in a tempestuous sea.

Round one was called. Woodruff and Buckley's second rushed in and half dragged them to their stools. Mooney and Donohue glided between the ropes. They made a great show of shivering as they pulled on their shirts and jackets. McShane was sitting in the two-wheeled gig, reins in one hand, whip in the other. Clancy with the money bag, Forman, Birdseye, Wilkinson, and the Shanahans had already mounted and gone. At a nod from McShane, Mooney and Donohue sprang into the gig. The timekeeper shouted "Time. Round two." Two white towels flashed into the mud-trodden ring. As the crowd converged on the gaming table to recover by force the money which McShane, Donohue and Mooney had won, McShane whipped the horse! The gig bounded and bounced down the rough, brush-bordered road. In his rear the crowd roared in pursuit.

From the salt works to Forman's it was about three miles of slippery snow and mud. The horse gained some, but the crowd was still in sight when the gig reached Forman's, just off the Seneca Turnpike. Forman stood in the driveway waving McShane eastward, shouting that Clancy was riding with the money toward the bunk house at Caldwell's Swamp. Without stopping McShane swerved eastward, pushing the horse to increased effort. A last glance backward told that some of the crowd were on horseback. A few had found carts. They did not pause at Forman's. They knew who had the money and they meant to catch him.

When McShane arrived at the bunk house, a few minutes ahead of the crowd, Clancy was placing a bulging canvas bag on a chopping block a few yards from the open doorway. He had included a dollar bill in the drawstring tied around the neck. Clancy waved and shouted, "The money is hidden, Mr. McShane. The bag is stuffed with chips and shavings. Hi lads! All out for the McShane. Grab a spare axe handle or pick handle, a shovel, or just a stick. The Sassenach are upon us."

McShane drove the gig into the deep shadow of the shed, sprang out, grabbed up an armful of thick round pieces of kindling wood and tossed them to his men as they poured out of the bunk house. He shouted, "Down the lane and hide behind the trees or bushes if you can find 'em. Don't stir till I give the battle cry. Then let 'em have it. Give it to 'em and no quarter."

McShane stood behind the bag. Mooney, Donohue, Clancy, Casey, and O'Brien, all wearing brass knuckles, crouched in support. From far down the lane the Salt Boilers caught sight of the bag and howled. In an irregular mass they panted up the lane, each eager to be first to seize the bag. Delaying until they were upon him, McShane snatched the bag and pretended to run for the shed. As they were flinging their arms around him and tearing at him he tossed the bag up on the flat shed roof and laid about him with his kindling wood.

Men who have lost their wind from violent running, and heave and labor to recover, are in no condition to fight. Also they were distracted by that bag balanced on the edge of the roof. McShane knocked them out with a sharp rap apiece behind the ear, but others came and swarmed all over him punching, kicking, and biting. A few of his supporters near him had sunk under the sheer weight of numbers before McShane roared, "Erin go Bragh!"

Trapped in the lane, hemmed in, whacked and swatted by experts, Salt Boilers everywhere were going down screaming. McShane suddenly became inspired by the lengths of twine thriftily hung on pegs when cut from the bales of fodder fed to the draft animals. Snatching handfuls, he deftly bound the fallen Salt Boilers. His men, knowing that their pay was in hand, were in a festive mood. Trained from infancy in the arts of assault and mayhem they were in their element. The Salt Boilers were rough and tough, but the Irish surpassed them. They were virtuosos. Their demoniac fury turned the fight into a flight.

McShane recalled his men. With help he had trussed fourteen Salt Boilers and stood them up against the sunny wall of the bunk house. He entered the house and came out with a jug of whiskey. Stepping off fifteen paces, he drank from the jug, packed a snow ball, threw it at an unsuspecting Salt Boiler and hit him squarely in the face.

The men followed McShane's example. Whiskey flowed and snow balls flew, and not only at the Salt Boilers! After months of day and night labor the men needed the release of a general snow ball fight.

At dusk Pippa rode in calling, "Boys will be boys," and "Aren't you having fun, building the canal?"

All sport ceased. The men silently trooped into the bunk house and built up the fires in the stoves. To McShane Pippa explained, "I came riding out this way to see how you were getting on. At Chittenango I heard there was to be a prize fight. So I galloped the rest of the way, but I must be too late. You look as though you've had it."

With a long stick McShane knocked the bag of wood chips down from the roof, dumped it out in plain view of the captive Salt Boilers, ordered Clancy to bring the money, and then refilled the bag and bound it to the back of Pippa's saddle. Then he spoke.

"We won this money from the Salt Boilers in fair fighting. Ride all night, Colleen, and in the morn deposit the money in the bank in Utica. Send me by mail a deposit paper and a package or two of blank bank drafts so that I can pay the men. By tomorrow there'll be so many Salt Boilers skulking hereabouts that we couldn't get the money out. Right now is the only time. Here's a bit of bread for you. 'Tis all we have. Come back to us at Christmas. And now be off. We'll be working tomorrow."

Pippa flushed, turned pale, then nodded. "All right, Mr. McShane. I guess my arrival was providential. Those Salt Boilers you are using for targets, seeing the money go, will tell the others after they're released. Then you won't be bothered. But what a wonderful day you've had. Let's always refer to this as the snow ball day."

After she had gone there was a general growl and murmur about entrusting all of that money to a young woman.

McShane spoke tersely, "Would any man here trust any other man with it? Everyone who doesn't come from Tipperary has a prison record."

The growl continued but on a different note. Perhaps the woman was honest, but with all that money she'd surely be waylaid before she reached Utica. At that point O'Brien's dissenting voice was heard.

"What? With all them knives she carries? Before a footpad could lay hand on the money bag, there'd be two knives in him so deep you could scarce see the handles. And, if he had a confederate, there'd be two more knives going his way so fast he couldn't dodge 'em. Before leaving the spot she'd rob the footpads and ride off leaving behind that silvery laugh of hers."

*　*　*　*

Six days later a properly executed and signed deposit paper, for an amount of money, somewhat in excess of what McShane had expected, arrived with blank bank drafts in the mail.

McShane sat down with quill and ink and paid wages in full to each man by signed draft. Afterward he paid his bills for supplies, also by draft. There was still a balance left. McShane invested it in many jugs of whiskey. After the whiskey had been delivered he made one of his rare speeches. Raising a jug he said,

"Lads, this has something the taste of Irish whiskey. I propose a toast to the colleen who made all this possible by getting that Salt Boiler money into the Utica bank. Pippa go Bragh!"

Chapter 4

THE FOREST FLOOR around the Walton Tract was freezing, but late autumn lingered in Caldwell Swamp. Canvass White had come to see how McShane would cut a channel through the swamp and make it stay cut.

Hummock-studded, stagnant pools warmed by springs still reflected irregular outlines of tufted bushes and the denuded boles of scattered dead maples. From the heavy overcast a wedge of ducks slipped down into the blue haze above the swamps, circled, and quacked off southward. Standing on the dry bank six feet above the swamp basin, McShane and Canvass White watched them. White remarked, "A sign of coming cold weather when those birds don't stop."

"Belike. And a sign of the almshouse closing, if I don't get my men back to work soon. They've formed habits of idleness already."

White's gaze came to rest on the twelve-foot lock of shining new limestone thirty-feet long and fifteen wide which would someday lower boats from the eastern ground level into the prehistoric lake bottom, now become a swampy district called Walton Tract. He spoke.

"Were those lock gates swung by Marshal Lewis, the little fellow who's so full of ideas? Or did David Bates swing them after he built the lock? I see you have them closed. Wouldn't it be better to leave them open to drain the channel into the low land and keep the banks from caving in? Those cave-ins spoil your prism. And it's a fine prism you've made all the way."

"Sure now it is that, but I must chance it. I need a

foot or two of water in the channel so that I can have an ice slide. I'll be needing those trees we pulled down and dragged aside when we were digging the channel, and more that I'll cut on both sides of the canal line. I plan to square the logs after cutting them into seven-foot lengths. We'll drag the squared logs on the ice in the channel, around the lock, slide them down on to frames and saw them into two-inch planks. The channel across the Walton Tract will have no prism, just a wall of tongued and grooved planks on each side driven straight down two feet into the mud by a pile driver. Twelve inches of plank will stick up above the water and hold back the mud of tow path and berm. Water in the mud will leach down leaving for the tow path sound, dry earth."

"That will require a lot of work, McShane."

"Work? Sure 'tis the only way to get the canal built. Happen there'll be some days in the winter when we can't stand the cold wind, but we'll be digging past the salt works, a mile or so to the south come spring."

"Where's your pile driver?"

"I've ordered two rectangular blocks of iron, three hundred pounds each, and each with a big iron ring at one end, also plenty of inch rope and enough six-inch, hand-forged spikes. We'll build two pile driver frames of two-by-fours and four-by-fours and pry them along on the surface, as we drive the planks in a solid row on each side of the channel. Each plank will project six inches above the water. A spirit level will be laid on the projecting ends, and a sledge hammer will even them up. The pile drivers will be raised by a ratchet and handle on one end of a shaft and, of course, a trip to drop the hammer."

"After you've driven your parallel rows of planks, what then?"

"We dig between them forty-feet wide at the top and the bottom and four-feet deep, throwing the earth and mud over the tops of the planks. They'll hold it from sliding back."

"But when the weight of mud is against the planks, won't they lean toward the channel?"

"No, because we peg lengths of two-by-twos along the tops of the planks like a coping and lay foot-thick logs parallel to the coping ten feet out. We'll lay poles across from coping to log every ten feet and spike them down at each end. The poles will look something like the rungs of a ladder lying on the ground. The dirt thrown out of the channel afterward will cover the logs and the poles to a depth of several inches."

For a few days White examined the forest southwest of the salt works, then rode back to Albany. He went to convince the Canal Commissioners that it would be practical to move the canal line, as it extended west of Camilus, southward to skirt the hill which stood three hundred and forty-two feet above the plain rather than cut through the soft swampy ground north of it. The northward line was shorter and more direct, but a channel dug there would tend to fill with mud. The southern route by skirting the base of a range of hills stretching westward to Jordan would be on firm soil and would include Nine Mile and Carpenter creeks as feeders.

After White had gone, Judge Joshua Forman rode into camp. The drooping corners of his mouth conveyed the impression that he was convinced something could never be done; the sag of his shoulders expressed defeat. Over a mug of tea he explained to McShane that he had been thinking things over, and it seemed that the farther west construction and channel digging might go, the more difficult it would all become. There would be no way to keep the men supplied with food, tools, and necessaries. Right now, no more digging could be done until the next summer. Then if swamp fever became endemic, as during the past two summers, so many of the workers might be affected that little could be accomplished. Judge Forman shook his head gloomily.

"You might cross the twelve miles of marshy ground in the Walton Tract by building an embankment all the way. But how deep in the mud would you have to go on either side of Onondaga Creek before hitting hard pan to base the foundations for a stone arch to carry the ditch and the tow path across? And you can't do it anyway, with the fever in summer and the snow in winter."

There was indeed snow, but in the canal line crossing the Walton Tract the soil beneath was frozen no deeper than two inches, barely enough to support oxen dragging an improvised snow plow. Oxen and horses also dragged a continuous line of logs along the bottom of the eastward channel to the sawing frames flanking the new lock. Other teams dragged stone boats loaded with blocks from the foot of a snow chute six miles westward. The quarry men at Split Rock were sending blocks down the chute on small sleds. Horse drawn bob-sleighs, some from Sullivan with barrels of cement and others from the Salt Works with salt, were coming into the crossings of Limestone and Butternut creeks on a short transverse from Seneca Turnpike. Salt would keep the concrete from freezing.

The snoring of many saws in different keys, and out of rhythm, was incessant day and night. Planks, timbers, and slabs fell from the sawing frames like ripe wheat before a scythe and were immediately carried to the forms being built at the creek crossings and to the pile driver frames.

As soon as the pile drivers were in action a clamor for more planks arose; logs were not arriving fast enough! McShane tramped around the Walton Tract hiring farmers who had horses, or a horse, to go miles eastward along the tow path and berm to pick up the neatly stacked logs his gangs had left. Farmers who were ill, or too occupied to go, were banged on the head until they recovered their health, or found time. Willingly or unwillingly, they all went, not the next day but as fast as they could harness and hitch, regardless of the hour. Sometimes a swift kick in the pants was required to start them.

In the nightly illumination of big bonfires, forms were built at both crossings. Stone arches for the tow path and long stone piers to support the wooden trunks (troughs) which would carry the channel over the crossing followed. Both pile drivers were sinking tongued and grooved plank walls on both sides of the channel. Black muck was being thrown out. Crude wooden pumps with plungers cut from the legs of worn-out leather boots spewed muddy water over the snow.

One bitter night when the operation was in full swing, Judge Forman came to watch it and wonder how he would be able to sleep when it reached Onondaga Creek. He called it McShane's Inferno and asked him when the men slept. McShane replied that when it was zero, and the wind was blowing, they all crawled into the bunk houses, built fires in the stoves, and slept until the wind stopped.

By the time the aqueducts over Butternut and Limestone had been built and the channel like a black scar had crept three miles into the Walton Tract, all of the logs stacked in the canal eastward for a distance of four miles had been hauled. To haul them a greater distance would have been uneconomical. However, trees in the canal line through the swampy Walton Tract were stunted and without lumber value.

On the southern hill slopes within yards of the canal line stood thousands of fat hemlocks. Without bothering to inquire about ownership, McShane ordered his men, and the reluctant farmers, to saw them down, trim, slice into logs, and drag to new sawing frames which he was having built at the base of the slopes. At once plank production increased so rapidly that he had a quantity hauled to Onondaga Creek. He transferred the gangs who had built the feeder dam and long ditch on Limestone Creek, and the aqueducts gangs, to begin work on an all-stone aqueduct across the swamp stream, Onondaga Creek. Because the old bunk houses were now too far away he began new ones on the high ground west of Onondaga Creek.

Everything was running smoothly when a young deputy sheriff, wearing a pistol in a holster, rode up and threatened an attachment on all of McShane's equipment to cover the value of trees he had stolen from the hillside. He served him with a summons to appear in court at Whitestone on the 25th of the following month and show his authority for taking trees from property not included in the canal survey. Until then he must cease from further activities. The deputy's manner was belligerent.

McShane grasped the bridle. With his other hand he took the summons paper and read it. At length he said, "Sure young feller, this is an Oneida County summons. To be valid in Onondaga County it should bear the signature of Judge Forman. Here, take the paper to him for signature. When you bring it back counter-signed, I'll accept service."

Without taking back the paper the young deputy said fiercely, "I don't have to. You have it."

"Sure I do. But with my other hand I'm holding your horse. That makes me a servant of yours and in your employ. The summons describes me as a contractor. I can't be both at the same time."

The deputy shouted, "But you're not my servant."

"Then I'm a contractor, and you are a trespasser on a section of public right-of-way in construction under my supervision. I have authority to commandeer horses in the public interest. Dismount. Your face is dirty. Thereby you set a bad example for my men. Hi, O'Brien! I'd like to see what this man looks like. Wash his face with snow."

As O'Brien advanced the deputy paled. "Give me that summons, Mr. McShane. Where can I find Judge Forman?"

McShane returned the paper, but retained the bridle. "Tis not far, but the way is intricate. If you'll take Mr. O'Brien on your horse's crupper, he'll guide you. And if he falls off, don't worry. O'Brien will find his way back."

O'Brien mounted and locked his arms around the deputy's middle. McShane started the horse with a slap that nearly unseated both riders. Scarcely were they out of sight when O'Brien reappeared on foot. In McShane's waiting hand he placed the attachment and summons. McShane laid them on a bonfire, remarking, "You may keep his watch and money, O'Brien, until he returns and asks for them. I doubt if he will, but give them to him if he does."

"Sure, it's too bad for the young feller. What will he say to Sheriff Cooper?"

"The truth. That he was robbed of his valuables and papers."

"And Sheriff Cooper?"

"He'll report the matter to Talcott. It's likely that Talcott will oppose force with force. We might see him out here in a week or so leading the Salt Boilers against us. Spread the word, O'Brien, that I want the men at all times to have clubs handy, until this persecution is over. Meanwhile I'll ask Judge Forman about who owns these timbered slopes."

On a melting day early in March McShane took a direct hit in the face from a snow ball thrown by a Salt Boiler hiding behind a tree. Concomitantly the air became filled with pelting snow balls, imprecations, and threats. Without warning the adjacent woods had filled with Salt Boilers. Action had begun.

Wearing felt-lined boots, cape, and fur-lined cap and gloves, Talcott rode from the deep shadow of the woods

into the glare of sunlight and snow. In ringing tones he
declared in the name of the law that he had a bench warrant for the return to prison of all of McShane's men and for
the detention of McShane himself.

The Salt Boilers supported his statement with cheers
and cat-calls.

McShane, with bowed head and drooping shoulders,
advanced slowly to meet him. Halting when Talcott was
in line between himself and the principal source of snow
balls, he asked,

"And the charge?"

"You are charged with stealing a great deal of money
from certain deputized gentlemen of the Salt Works, whose
names are listed, on the afternoon of the first Tuesday in
last December. By subpoena of the records of the Utica
Bank we have proof of your high-handed conduct."

More cheers from the "gentlemen of the Salt Works."
The Irish continued to work, paying Talcott and his followers no attention. McShane proudly lifted his head and
spoke in an even voice.

"Sir, those arboreal creatures behind you which in sun-
nier clime would be throwing coconuts, but in this latitude
throw snow balls from concealment at the unsuspecting,
are they the redoubtable Salt Boilers?"

From the forest fringe came howls of derision and
another burst of snow balls, well-aimed, but, falling short,
they found target mostly on the rear of Talcott's horse. The
horse whinnied, lashed with its tail, bared its teeth, and
took off eastward.

McShane watched, then turned to his men and said, "All
right lads. Take the monkeys."

The speed of Talcott's horse convinced McShane that
if Talcott should wish to return he would have to come on
foot, thereby losing prestige and dignity. McShane immediately recalled his men. They obeyed reluctantly. McShane

comforted them by explaining that the Salt Boilers had such a head start that they couldn't have been caught. Thus much work time would have been lost. Instead, no work time that night and songs after supper with whiskey aplenty.

Two weeks later McShane received a notice from the bank in Utica that his small cash balance had been impounded pending execution of a warrant. With a feeling of impending doom McShane consulted Judge Forman.

Forman confided that the title to the slopes from which McShane was still cutting trees was not clear. Had he stopped when he was first warned, the matter might have been dropped. Now it was likely that a U.S. Marshall would come from Albany with a Cease and Desist order which McShane must observe until there could be a court ruling, or the State acquired the land and then gave him permission.

McShane shook his head and said that so much time would be lost that the dug channel could not reach Montezuma that year. Thus the Regency would have accomplished its purpose. He then asked Forman to send his clerk Wilkinson on horseback to the Salt Works to invite Richmond or Woodruff or Buckley to come for a conference with McShane. The Irish were facing trouble and needed the aid of the Salt Boilers. Two hours later Wilkinson returned with all three.

When everyone was seated and hot coffee laced with whiskey had been served, McShane spoke.

"The Judge tells me that you are after shipping your salt by way of the Seneca and Oswego rivers and Canadian waters. It must be slow and expensive."

Richmond, sitting erect with arms straight in front, hands resting on knees and a hard look in his gray eyes, nodded. The other two nodded slightly.

"Sure now it lies within your power, and 'tis for you to

say, that this summer, only three months from now, you could ship by canal from your Salt Works to German Flatts on the Mohawk River. There you'd be having a transfer to bateaux and a down river haul to Schenectady where freight wagons on a good road would carry your casks to Albany, which is an ocean port."

McShane paused. The three still sat rigidly erect, but, instead of staring into space, they were looking at him. He continued, "My contract includes a lateral canal from the main channel to your works. But I don't have to build it until a year from this spring. It will help your business if I build it this spring, and I shall—if I can get some help from you."

In a booming voice Richmond asked, "What help?"

"I need timbers and planks and twenty-foot logs for piles to build bases and forms for arches across Onondaga Creek. I need money to buy stone blocks and cement for the aqueduct. I'll need thousands of two-inch planks for the tongue and groove construction across the marl meadows and up to the salt works. The Regency has tied up my capital. The state is far behind in paying me what it owes. The judge here says I'm about to be enjoined from cutting timbers anywhere but in the canal line."

The three relaxed, glanced at each other, and whispered.

Richmond asked, "Where do you expect us to get all of this timber?"

"Where do you cut the wood you use for fuel to do your boiling?"

"We own a few acres of woodland."

"Wouldn't it be worth five thousand logs to have canal transportation this summer for your salt going south and east?"

"What else?"

"No money. But tons of pork, beans, peas, flour, potatoes,

and jugs of whiskey. Invoice the food to us to be paid when the state pays us."

"What else?"

"Sure now, come and have a supper and musical evening with us once in a while. You might know some stories and new jigs. Bring your friends. If we have a bit of tobacco, we'll share it with you. We're poor, but we enjoy life."

The three rubbed their chins, scratched their ears, glanced at each other, and nodded.

Richmond arose and offered his hand. "We'll go you, McShane. Three days from now we'll deliver to you, where the canal crosses Onondaga Creek, two hundred logs daily. And we'll help you saw them into planks at the same rate you pay your men and trust you until you are paid by the state. How about a little wrestling on those social evenings?"

McShane shook hands with each of the three murmuring, "I don't know why you're doing all this for me."

Buckley spoke up sharply, "We aren't. We don't like the Regency any better than you do. When we saw you getting that there Talcott between yourself and us, we knew what you wanted us to do and we done it. Didn't we?"

"Sure now, the horse thought so."

         o   o   o   o

Deprived of the services of a bank, McShane made himself a wooden strongbox which he secured with a borrowed padlock. In the box he kept his last bit of currency, enough to meet one payroll. He had to have someplace where O'Brien couldn't get it. A few days later it occurred to him that an even better way would be to send O'Brien to New York to pick up another hundred Irishmen. When he gave him the order he also gave him five silver dollars for expenses.

Accepting the five dollars reluctantly, O'Brien spoke in a hurt tone, "Sure now, J.J., you'll not be sending me to New York with but five dollars in my pocket?"

"Along the road, O'Brien, a sharp lad like you will see many opportunities to buy and sell pigs and chickens at a long profit. You may keep whatever you make, if you bring me a hundred Irishmen and no excuses. Away with you before you have the money in my pocket which I'm saving for next payroll."

O'Brien started then returned. "Did you say 'next payroll?'"

"Aye."

O'Brien handed McShane a roll of bank notes. "If that's the money you're saving to pay the lads, or think that you are, take it, give it to them, and tell them that I wanted them to have it."

Chapter 5

A Scottish encyclopedia containing a detailed description and diagrams, which belonged to someone in Albany, was the only plan of a canal lock that could be found in New York State. Canvass White was the only native New Yorker who had seen a lock such as was used in England, and McShane was the only man who had been employed in England in building one. David Bates, an arrogant sarcastic native, had copied the texts and drawings from the encyclopedia and had learned what he could from questioning McShane. Bates' obsession was to become the leading lock engineer and authority—let others wear away their youth and strength in digging, filling, and constructing wooden forms for stone arches and trunks to carry water across streams and rivers. Without locks, the five-hundred-foot fall between Lake Erie and the Hudson River would have made a continuous canal impossible. So the canal needed locks. The locks needed Bates.

With the bursting of buds and the peeping of small frogs in large swamps, rumors began to run back and forth along the canal line. Ara Broadwell was building an eleven-foot lock at Nine Mile Creek; John and Sam Horne another at Skaneatles Creek. Murray and McNab were sinking piles upon which they would lay a mat topped with grouting as the foundation for a lock on section sixty-four. Luther Doolittle was having difficulty with lock construction at Owasco Outlet. In desperation Benjamin Wright, superintendent of all construction on the Erie Canal, being unable to get an order from the Canal Commissioners nominating Bates as engineer in charge of locks, told Bates to go to Doolittle's assistance. Either the Commissioners would confirm the appointment or there would be a row. Wright rather hoped for a row, because only from the flames of a row could the golden phoenix of a settled policy be born.

Having completed Onondaga Creek aqueduct, a baffling construction because of the great weight of so much stone upon yielding mud, McShane, ignoring rumors, dug a channel along the base of the southern hills. He crossed the marl meadows southwest of the Salt Works, dug the lateral canal he had promised the Salt Boilers, continued northwesterly, then bent to the southwest over the flat land. He built an all-stone aqueduct of five arches across Nine Mile Creek, and, while building, sent half of his weary force on to dig around the point of a big hill and northwestward between two more hills to a long narrow swamp; thence west to Jack's Reef.

At Nine Mile McShane sacrificed a few of his insufficient sleeping hours to advise Ara Broadwell about the way he was building a lock. Piles had been properly driven, mat laid and overlaid with grouting. The lock walls had been built six-feet thick, cemented, buttressed, and faced in front. The corners were squared. However, Ara was in despair because he couldn't find a way to set his gate posts so that they would hold.

With a hammer and chisel McShane made the beginning cut of a hollow quoin at each frontal inside corner of the lock walls. When chiselled all the way down, hollows were formed into which the gate posts would fit. After the posts had been cramped to the stone blocks with iron bands, the gates, always lubricated by water, could be opened and closed by their gears quite slowly. This construction was repeated at the other end of the lock chamber. From a nearby surface ledge, McShane cut enough long rectangular blocks eight-inches thick to cope the walls. Coping protected the cement, which joined the blocks beneath, from penetration by rain and frost and consequent bulging of the wall. The last touches were lock culverts and ventilators.

When Ara thanked McShane profusely for his kindness, McShane retorted that he hadn't helped Ara because he was pretty, but because he wanted him to go back to Harbor Creek and build a six-foot lock on the east side of the creek and then admit the creek to the channel as a feeder. The lock was necessary to lift boats from the swamp level of the Walton Tract to the base-of-the-hill level which began at that point.

Ara's smiling thanks turned to growling grumbles. He complained that under guise of doing him a favor, McShane had slipped a sharp bargain over on him. McShane's reply was to kick him in the pants and follow with a sharp slap in the same place with the blade of a shovel. Ara took the hint. As he left, McShane shouted after him that Dexter Pease and Mosley of Split Rock Quarry would, upon application, supply him with stone blocks.

Before McShane reached Jack's Reef, Ara returned and stated in a sarcastic tone that he had built the lock. McShane merely nodded and remarked that Ara could build a lock at Jordan and be paid for it. Ara brightened, then drooped when McShane added, "If you'll go back to Harbor

Creek and build me a thirty-foot canal boat right in the lock and paint in green letters on the bow the name 'Shamrock.'"

Ara gave McShane an odd look and complied.

A few days later Benjamin Wright rode westward from his home at Fairmount to see how McShane was progressing. McShane presented to him the plan of closing the drains in the channel from Utica to Jack's Reef. The banks had had time to settle. This would be a good opportunity to test the banks for weak spots by admitting water from the feeders to the full depth of four feet in the channel.

Unconvinced, Wright reminded McShane that water would come at full depth to the face of the digging and stop further construction. McShane countered that a coffer dam of sheet piling could be set right across the channel thirty feet from the face of the digging and be banked with earth on both sides. The earth would hold the sheet piling erect and on the east side hold back the water. The *Shamrock* would bring food and clothing from Utica, cement from Chittenango, and stone blocks from Cossitts, the port for Split Rock Quarry.

Wright's brow still puckered. How would the coffer dam be moved forward when the face of the digging had advanced a few miles?

McShane explained that a duplicate coffer dam would be built and set up in similar fashion a few feet behind the advancing face of the digging and similarly banked on both sides with earth. Then the earth banked against the first dam would be scooped out with shovels and wooden buckets. The dam would be lifted. The water would rush in and float the wooden dam as far as the second dam, where it would be hauled out and dragged ahead to the advanced face of further digging. There it would be set up in the channel as before. This leapfrogging of coffer dams would keep the *Shamrock* in touch with the westward-receding face of the digging.

After a few more questions Wright nodded approval of the plan. McShane suggested that he would like to ask a question. Would the canal terminate at Seneca River, or would the legislature authorize the extension of it to Lake Erie? Wright fished a newsclipping from the tail pocket of his coat and said, "Mr. McShane, during a discussion in the legislature about levying taxes on lands contingent to the canal to defray in part the ever-mounting costs of excavation and construction, that question was asked. Governor Clinton answered it. His speech is reproduced in this news clipping." Wright read aloud, "Notwithstanding the conviction of the Commissioners that the canals can be made without any serious inconvenience to the financial operation of the State, yet they are persuaded that it is due to the counsels of prudence to bring the solidity of their opinions to the touchstone of experiment before the whole system is undertaken."

McShane took in a deep breath. "Sure now the Governor is well educated in words, but could you tell me what he means by the touchstone of experiment?"

"If you dig your channel to Montezuma before winter, and David Bates finishes a lock to connect the canal with Seneca River, and you build a plank and cribwork bridge across Seneca River to serve as a tow path, cut away the brush on the west bank of the Seneca to Canandaigua Outlet—a smooth stream deep enough for canal boats—and clean the brush from the north bank all the way to Canandaigua Lake, and finish the clearing by January of eighteen-hundred-and-twenty, and a boat goes all the way from Utica to Canandaigua Lake the following May—that will be the touchstone of experiment. Why? Because Canandaigua Lake is only eighty miles east of Lake Erie."

"Sure now, would the counsels of prudence and the solidity of opinions be satisfied?"

"Unquestionably. If before next April we can do the things I have just mentioned, the legislature will pass an act extending the canal to Lake Erie, and the canal law will be amended accordingly. Senator Martin Van Buren would propose the amendment."

"Van Buren? He heads the Regency."

"Yes. The Regency was sure that the canal would never be dug west of Rome. By the end of the year eighteen-seventeen we had made what we considered our best effort. The line between Utica and Rome—the only easy stretch between Lake Erie and the Hudson—was like a dotted line of poorly dug, unfinished ditches. The Regency was elated. Then, Heaven bless the Irish, you came the next year. And now that you will in a few weeks complete over a hundred miles of navigable channel what can the Regency do, to save face, but extend the limit to Lake Erie? The difficulties you have met so far are boys' games compared to crossing the great Cayuga Marsh, the deep Irondequoit Valley, the Genesee River, the even deeper valleys west of Brockport, and the mountain ridge of dolomite limestone, sixty-feet high and nine-miles wide, called Tonawanda Summit. The Regency will try to give you a task which they are sure you can't perform. It's their only way out."

"And if we do it?"

"That will end the Regency, of course. I'm not a religious man, McShane, but after you go west of Montezuma say your prayers every night. And encourage all of your men to believe that God is at their right hand, because with all the magnificent resourcefulness, hardihood, and courage of the Irish they'll need God's help, and a lot of it. And so will you. Good Luck, McShane, and the luck of the Irish."

*　　*　　*　　*

After the drains in the channel from Utica to Jordan

had been closed, the feeder gates were opened in all the little streams which crossed the canal. When water had been impounded over the entire stretch, the *Shamrock* carrying a repair crew with tools and a small amount of food was hauled eastward by a team of worn-out horses. Returning westward the men found and repaired many weak spots in the banks, where they were crumbling from the contact of water. The crew cut and drove stakes into the widening gulf, interwove the stakes with branches, poles, or vines, and restored the bank with a fill of earth and stones reenforced with layers of branches and cut bushes. The repairs, though well made, unavoidably destroyed the prism, or contour of the channel, in those particular spots. The stakes would likely snag a tow rope, but they could be removed as soon as the bank had solidified.

Two weeks later the *Shamrock* returned with a stock of food, stone blocks from Split Rock for the Jordan lock, and Pippa strumming the tune of an Irish jig. The crew were jigging on the stone blocks. The boy driving the team was prancing as he walked.

McShane helped Pippa off the boat by catching her when she jumped. As he set her on her feet he muttered something about frivolity. Regarding him sternly, she handed him an Albany newspaper, the *Argus.** McShane glanced at the headlines. His eyes traveled on to the men in the boat.

"Have they seen this?"

She tossed her thick golden hair. "Of course. They gave it to me. They were all for quitting and returning to New York when they saw in the paper that just before adjournment the legislature voted each of the Canal Commission-

---

* The *Argus* was known as a Van Buren newspaper. It favored the Regency. It was established in 1813.

ers, who have thus far served for nothing, an annual salary
of twenty-five hundred dollars. They did it because the
Commissioners have made such headway in constructing
the canal that they deserve to be rewarded. For example,
because of the oversupply of labor they hope to reduce
costs by paying men twenty-seven cents a day instead of
thirty-five.

"The *Shamrock* men said that it was not the Commissioners, sitting all day with their feet on their desks and
smoking cigars, who have made headway in construction.
It's the rugged Irish, working all winter in thin, worn
clothes in the bitter winds and in icy swamp water in
broken boots from dawn until dark seven days a week, who
have built the canal after everyone had about given it up.
I diverted them by making them dance, but the news will
spread; and you, J.J., will soon have labor trouble."

"I'm having trouble now. They're bringing in Nolan.
He's bleeding."

After one look Pippa ran for her baggage. Over her
shoulder she called, "I brought a tent and two folding cots,
also a scissors, bandages, and medicines. Help me to raise
the tent."

The two men who had brought Nolan laid him on the
ground and returned unconcernedly to their work. With the
tent and cots in service Pippa helped McShane to lay
Nolan on a cot. He had an ugly foot wound from a glancing axe. Pippa pulled off a boot and sock, washed the
wound, sprinkled it with powdered herbs, sewed it together,
and bandaged it. Then she spread a sheet over his legs to
keep the flies off, gave him a drink of whiskey, and his
pipe and tobacco. By that time another man had arrived
with a wood splinter in his right eye. Pippa extracted the
splinter, and the man returned to work.

For the next few days as a feeling of injustice sank into
the men's hearts they became sullen and slowed in their

work. Beautiful, sparkling Pippa with a sweet smile and an appreciation of Irish wit checked a demonstration with which McShane could hardly have coped. But the men were unhappy.

After several trips to Cossitts and back, traveling continually day and night, the *Shamrock* brought in enough stone blocks and kegs of cement to finish the lock at Jordan. Meanwhile the tree pullers and channel diggers had gone on toward Weedsport. Pippa urged McShane to send the *Shamrock* to Utica for onions, beets, and other fresh vegetables, and for medical supplies. McShane grumbled. There were other things which he needed more. But he gave in.

The *Shamrock* had been gone for six days. The tension in McShane's camps and bivouacs had continued to mount despite Pippa's best efforts. At night mosquitoes were so persistent that sleep was impossible. Pippa wanted the men to rub their faces, necks, and hands with sweet oil and penny royal, claiming that it would drive away the mosquitoes, but they sullenly ignored her. A few men were prostrated with swamp fever. The eastward-flowing Seneca River was now parallel to the westward-digging forward gangs and only two or three miles north of them. Swamps lined both banks of the Seneca River. Many of the mosquitoes were small, black, and stood on their heads on the walls of the tent, bark shelter, or any vertical surface upon which they might alight.*

At the close of a day, when each hour had been more tense than the last, McShane broke a grim silence by explaining to Pippa that the Irish were immune to hardship, exhaustion, and danger, but just couldn't work if they were unhappy or wanted to fight. Unless something happened soon, they would be fighting each other, and that would end their efficiency so far as the canal was concerned.

---

* Anopheles mosquitoes, carriers of malaria.

In a sympathetic tone Pippa said, "Isn't it time for the *Shamrock* to return?"

McShane shrugged. "I don't know. The boat might have run into trouble. Why?"

"When I was in Utica there was a rumor that O'Brien was shepherding a hundred Irish westward along the Mohawk Turnpike. He got them from the streets, the jails, and all sorts of places. They were said to be stealing from the farms—boots, clothes, pigs, chickens, anything they could lay their hands on. The sheriffs tried to restrain them, but were batted on their heads or thrown in the Mohawk River. A few old timers who could remember Indian raids during the American Revolution said that the Indians were tame compared to the Irish. That's why I wanted the *Shamrock* to return to Utica. I don't need more medicines. I wanted to have some conveyance in Utica to bring them here. But, J.J., considering the mood of your men, suppose the *Shamrock* should arrive tonight?"

McShane gripped her arm. "Listen! I hear singing. 'Tis the old Tipperary marching song 'The Bold McIntyres.' It is the *Shamrock*. The Saints be praised. Hey there! Light bonfires along the berm so that our lads can see to fight. Wake up everybody and call back the forward gangs. There're a hundred men from a southern county about to arrive and take your jobs away from you. They'll work for twenty cents a day. Why should I pay you leprechauns twenty-seven? Find your shillelaghs, lads. You'll need them."

In the uncertain light of newly kindled watch fires the *Shamrock* arrived with howling, taunting men completely filling the boat. Without waiting for the boat to stop the newcomers sprang to the shore and set about demolishing McShane's men. His men were tired and worn, but a mounting demoniac force which they had been repressing suddenly transformed them.

McShane led Pippa to a safe distance, then turned and

forgot her as he bellowed advice and encouragement to his men. From the *Shamrock* O'Brien urged his men on with skilled understanding. It was an Irish fight which ended with most of the combatants falling into the canal. No one was drowned, but the water did cool them. As they stood near the fires trying to get dry they saw Myron Holley, the paymaster, standing on the forward deck. McShane's men instantly recognized him and gave a cheer. Holley acknowledged the greeting with a short speech to the effect that newcomers would be paid twenty-seven cents a day until they had proved themselves. Twenty-seven cents was presently the prevailing day-rate for the whole canal line, but since McShane's men were now veterans they would henceforth receive forty cents a day. Bosses would be paid forty-five.

With a whiskey jug in one hand and a chunk of charcoal in the other, Pippa passed among the cheering, singing men marking the forehead of every veteran McShane man with the letter V and permitting him to seal it with a long pull at the jug. Holley placed his money bag on a table in Pippa's tent and opened his payroll book. Pippa opened her book of hours worked. A line formed. McShane called out the name of each man entitled to wages. The man stepped forward, made his mark, and received his money. Dice and card games started immediately and continued all night.

After breakfast they all went to work, the veterans happily training the new men. The new men, made hopeful by what they had heard and seen, tried to equal or surpass the veterans. The general mood was so cheerful that the men allowed Pippa to rub their faces and necks after supper with oil and penny royal. During the day their tobacco smoke drove away the mosquitoes.

During the onset of exuberant spirits and the subsequent festivities Pippa kept herself out of sight, but with the dawn she went about deftly applying cold mud packs to bruised faces and blackened eyes. As a consequence swellings receded, closed eyes opened, and work proceeded as usual. Once she caught the approving gaze of McShane, and he had the grace to confirm it with one of his rare, but qualified compliments.

"Sure, you're making yourself that useful I wouldn't know how to manage without you. But when do you find time to keep up the book work?"

Pippa fired back at him, "If you'd take a few minutes off from walking around and playing the harp and look at your books, you'd see that they are up."

McShane scowled, "Harp? What harp?"

"Oh, when finding fault with everybody and criticizing everything they do, and swearing besides, your voice has the plaintive sweetness of an Irish harp. In my opinion it's a misapplication and waste of talent."

McShane looked around quickly to see if any of the men were listening. The audience was extensive. Grins were ill-concealed.

Attracted by her spirited resourcefulness the men came to her with their troubles. To the sincere she was friendly, but the amorous left hurriedly and thereafter avoided her.

Feeling that she was needed and playing a small but important part, Pippa was happy. One day the *Shamrock* arrived with a cargo which included a small package of mail. One letter was for Pippa. The handwriting made her flush. She retired to her tent to open the letter. When she emerged she had a sealed, addressed letter which would go east on the *Shamrock's* next trip. To ease their curiosity she said to the men who were near, "To save you from stretching your necks so far that you'll never get them back to natural length, I'll say that my letter is addressed to Samuel Talcott in Utica. Mrs. Talcott has passed away, and now he wants to marry me."

With one voice they asked, "What did you say to him?"

"I said 'Yes.' I think he'll be coming for me fairly soon."

"And leave us?"

"And leave all of you. However, I like every man here. I don't wish to leave you. The decision was not easy."

Later, she saw McShane. He looked her in the eye and said, "Colleen, no woman can live happily with a man if she has a rival in his affections. Sometimes it's another woman. That division you could handle. In Talcott's case it will be a bottle of whiskey. If he has to choose, it will be the bottle. His wife was a young woman. Have you thought what may have caused her death?"

The impact of McShane's stern words forced Pippa's eyes down. When she looked up her expression was defiant.

"Samuel Talcott does have a weakness for liquor. He turned to whiskey because his wife nagged him unmercifully. He was too kind-hearted to rebuke her, although she tongue-lashed him whenever she saw him—often in public. You would have cured her by taking her over your knee. Mr. Talcott hunched his shoulders and bowed to the storms. As his wife I can wean him from the bottle and help him along in his chosen career of politics. He's the smartest lawyer in the United States and a born politician."

McShane shrugged and turned away. "You're free to go whenever you like."

Three weeks later Talcott rode into camp leading a horse with a side saddle and saddle bags. Talcott was wearing his usual gray suit and low-crowned, wide-brimmed gray hat. His face and neck were so red that they seemed to be afire. His nose was purple. The black mourning band on his left sleeve suggested that he had sorrows to drown— according to O'Brien. McShane happened to be absent arranging and lighting smudges to protect his men from mosquitoes, but upon his return O'Brien reported the incident.

"That Talcott! Sure I'd punch him in the nose if I wasn't afraid of burning my knuckles. There's something wrong about him. Otherwise, why is he always drinking rum out of a whiskey bottle?

"Sure, he stopped his horses before her tent and fell off the one he was riding. She came out of her tent looking good enough to take a bite out of. Talcott had got to his feet by climbing up his horse's front leg. By that time two or three dozen of the lads had gathered and stood leaning on their shovels with fool grins on their faces.

"At first Talcott paid them no attention. He tried to locate his hat on the ground. Then his gloved hand accidentally bumped into it on his head. He took it off, looked at it as if he'd never seen it before, cocked it at the proper angle, and made a low bow.

"Says I to myself, 'He'll never get that load of rum in his middle erect again.' Nor did he. When he finally straightened up, he'd left most of it on the ground. By that time some of the lads were grinning aloud. The girl silenced them with a glance. With his back to them Talcott addressed himself to her."

In falsetto O'Brien repeated Talcott's speech, " 'Now that I am single I'm proposing to you marriage. If you wish to be my wife, mount the spare horse. We'll ride beneath the leafy boughs to Utica while the birds carol a wedding march. Tomorrow before His Reverence we'll exchange our vows.'

"For such a fine speech the lads all clapped their hands. Talcott turned and seemed to see them all for the first time. So he waved his crop and shouted, 'Hurrah for the Irish! How much longer will you serve under the lash of the taskmasters of Egypt? By this time you should all be in politics. You're too fine and able to dig mud out here in the wilderness. Lay down your shovels. Stand up for your rights and higher pay.'

"The girl's face went pale. She tapped him on the shoulder. 'Sam Talcott, you drunken agitator. J. J. McShane has sweat blood for two years building up this fine work force. Now in two minutes you are trying to tear it down. It's a shame. I'm a part of these working men, and I'm remaining with them. Please, O'Brien, get him back on his horse and send him out of here.'

"We put Talcott on his horse and chased away Denny who was swinging at him with a hatchet. Talcott escaped with his horse, but we kept the other horse for her to ride. She returned to her tent, but in the doorway she looked back over her shoulder. The lads were going back to work. When they noticed her looking at them, they raised their muddy shovels and said 'Miss Post, go Bragh! We're for you.'

"She went into her tent and tied the flap. I could hear her crying. I still can't make up my mind whether she was crying from grief or joy."

A wintry smile lighted faintly McShane's faraway look. He ventured, "Neither, O'Brien. She was crying from relief. Sometimes a woman's eyes have to be washed with tears before she can see a man as he really is. Better to happen before the wedding, even with the lads all plastered with mud looking on, than afterward."

"Speaking of mud, J.J., have you been observing how we've been slowing down as we dig along the edge of this chain of long narrow swamps stretching to the Seneca River? And the chain is anything but straight. The men are digging clay mud. It's heavy, slippery, and hard to load. When they try to dump it, a third sticks to the barrow and has to be dug out. Slowly the mud slides back to where it has to be dug out again. It never stays anywhere until it dries. Now if you'd be sending men ahead to dig drainage ditches wherever there's standing water in the natural hollows of the untouched canal line, we'd be working in clay that is only damp and fine for packing down a good prism."

McShane reflected, then nodded. "Sometimes I think I can see some good in you, O'Brien. Here comes the girl. She walks as if she'd forgotten Talcott."

"She's waving a letter and all excited about it. Might be from him."

McShane shook his head. "If so, she wouldn't be dancing along like that. She's a canal girl now."

Pippa came up to them with a pucker between her glowing blue eyes. Thrusting the letter at McShane she said anxiously, "According to my books, we used all of our cement except a barrel and a half at Skaneatles Outlet. That leaves scarcely enough for cementing the blocks in a single arch across Cold Spring Brook at Weedsport. There will be none for the double arch at Owasco Outlet, nor for another single arch at Crane Brook near Montezuma. In that letter from Mr. Canvass White, which I took the liberty of opening, he writes that so much cement is being used east of Nail Creek near Utica and especially at Little Falls that he can't spare you any. He wonders if you can make some cement from the meagre limestone at Jack's Reef." She glanced at the letter. "He says you can recognize that type of limestone by its yellowish-gray color. He goes on to tell how to construct a kiln and fill it properly. After burning, the stone has a buff color and will be ten percent lighter. It will not slack like mortar. Then he describes the pounding and pulverizing until the stone is ground to powder. Before adding water the powder should be mixed with sand, half and half." She looked at McShane, "Can you do it?"

McShane nodded. "For a time I was employed by a cement company in England."

"Then I may write to Mr. Canvass White that you'll make enough cement for our needs?"

"Aye, and some to spare for the contractors eastward.

I'll go back to Jack's Reef myself with a gang. Sure, I'll teach them how to make cement. But who's to take over here while I'm away?"

Pippa stiffened. "If it's your wish, I will."

McShane looked at O'Brien. "Did you ever hear of such a thing?"

"Not for two hundred Irishmen. But I've heard of a wife bossing one man."

"One man is harder than two hundred. She can play the two hundred against each other. For a woman that's duck soup. But, if there should be another woman!"

"Sure, it would be Hell. Let's not talk about it."

* * * *

Given authority Pippa drove the men day and night. Only those ill with fever were permitted a full night's sleep after a twelve-hour day. Healthy men had to work eighteen hours. Regardless of obstructions, weather, or adversity they must dig the channel to the lock west of Montezuma which Bates had recently finished.

The men resented, then rebelled, but her furious will power drove them on. Her reputation for temper and speed with knives shielded her from physical violence. Word went round that she never slept, indeed had no cot in her tent. One man choosing a time when her tent was deserted and Pippa nowhere near, or so he thought, parted the door flaps and looked in to see whether she had a bed. He saw; but because of the butt of a heavy knife thrown accurately at the back of his neck, he was unable afterward to remember what he had seen.

* * * *

The leaves were falling when the *Shamrock*, having ferried enough cement and stone blocks for the arches at Cold Spring Brook, Owasco Outlet, and Crane Brook, arrived at

Montezuma with a full load of food supplies, boots, and warm clothing—and McShane.

Upon greeting O'Brien, McShane's first remark was, "Well, O'Brien, it seems that the lads have cut a canal through to Seneca River and are presently building a tow-path bridge. I'd like to find some fault, but I've examined the prism and found nothing to criticize."

"Sure, J.J., that's life. You can't have everything."

McShane frowned. "How did the girl get on with bossing the gangs?"

"Supported by the Tipperary Ten and guided by your long-suffering but faithful friend James O'Brien she managed, as you have seen. She played them against each other. She even tried it with me."

"Tried it? Hah!"

*   *   *   *

Next afternoon the cloud ceiling was slate blue and low. Pippa asked McShane to walk with her to a low hill almost a mile west of Montezuma where they could see the new lock which Bates had built and the stone and log crib-work piers which the men were building. Beyond the Seneca River stretched the great Cayuga Marsh, north, west, and south—an expanse of nodding, rustling cat tails, as far as they could see. Spears of gabbling geese and wedges of ducks streamed southward. A faint, cold breeze carried the pungent odor of swamp and pushed the brown heads of cat tails into ripples. McShane grumbled.

"Fluid mud. Nine miles of it. And when we try to cut a channel through it, the mud won't stay put."

With a side-long glance, Pippa said demurely, "Sheet piling on both sides of the channel and anchored by poles nailed to logs sunk in the mud twelve feet on each side."

"That will require ninety thousand planks. We can't saw them out and place that many by spring."

"If you mean just around, I'm sure you can't, for it'll be necessary," Mac rather told me, "at some way some boards are telling that there won't be room enough available to dig scores that are adequately mapped. They have to

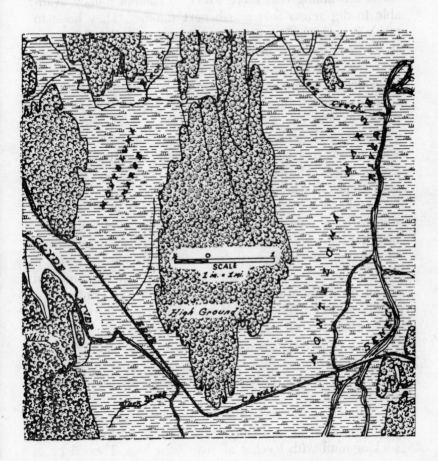

the ground with feeding all that area, but, Mac, to clean some pavilions or you that well know go to that best bench that will be impaired, and shut, and the waiting substituted if inland. When you come, you can draw from those poisonous belts. Mr. Ferguson, ... will fill up you all niche to anything wed down from the top and founda- tion, so, and your new pavilion, showing level, and lamp

"If you mean next spring, I'm sure you can't. Nor will it be necessary. Mr. Talcott told me that so many state banks are failing that there won't be enough money available to dig across that marsh next summer. They hope to tackle it in the spring of eighteen twenty-one. But they can't start them because nearly every spring the Seneca River rises two feet above the water in the marsh. So the marsh is flooded until almost July. Then the mosquitoes come, and they make work impossible. I advise you to saw as many planks as you can along Canandaigua Outlet, this winter and next, and stack them so that they will season. All the way across the big marsh the canal line runs close to Canandaigua Outlet. So you can conveniently transport your planks to wherever you'll need them."

McShane regarded her admiringly. "You're after doing well with my men while I was starting a cement works. I've been told already that but for your knives they'd have tried to kill you because you drove them so hard. Belike it couldn't have been done any other way. But why are you so set on digging across the big marsh in the winter?"

"Because I believe that if you should die, the engineers and other contractors all together would not have the courage, experience, and leadership to finish the canal all the way."

"Sure, Colleen, I don't expect to die in the next few years."

"I don't want you out there with your men in the blazing July sun, and no shade anywhere. You'll be in water and sucking-mud with leeches all over your legs. There'll be so many mosquitoes on you that you'll look as if you had brown fur. You'll be sunburned and thirsty, and the swamp water isn't fit to drink. When you return to your bunk house those poisonous little black mosquitoes will bite you all night. In a short time, worn down by hardship and exhaustion, you and your men will have swamp fever, and many of you will die. Those who survive will ask to be returned to jail to serve the rest of their terms."

"But Colleen, if I don't take the section, someone else with a gang of Irishmen will."

"Let 'em. Those who have never lived in a swamp in summer, as I have in Utica, don't know about the awful summer sickness. Our winters are cold, but they are healthy. A year from next spring all the canal contractors will be bidding for this section because it looks easy. They'll force down the contract price to break-even or less. Don't you bid. By the following August the workers will be dead or sick or running away.

"The Canal Commissioners will call for bids. They'll offer an ever higher price, but no one will bid. By September Governor Clinton will be in a desperate position. His enemies will be on his back, especially the Regency. At that moment if some well-known contractor should step forward and offer to dig a canal channel from this lock down around May's Point and straight across the marsh to the Mead farm and have the whole eleven (not nine) miles open for navigation by summer of eighteen twenty-two, he could have it at his price. You, J.J., would be the man of the hour."

McShane looked down into her sparkling deep blue eyes. "Sure, you have me more than half convinced. But why so much outspoken interest in a hard-shell old Irishman who couldn't hold a cup of tea in a parlor without spilling it?"

Pippa blushed. Her long blond lashes went down. She started to speak, faltered, then began again.

"I don't know whether you understand a young woman's heart. Assuming that you don't, I'll say that many healthy girls of about my age select some man for reasons of their own and form an attachment for him. Some girls lead their men on to a proposal of marriage, then pretend to be shocked and angry, which they are not at all. Others waiting, like me, try to occupy their time with a diverting task such as the canal. A few seize their men and propose to them.

"Once a woman in her twenties has formed an attachment for a man, she is caught forever in a web of her own spinning. Neither she nor her devoted friends can break the spell. But the idol she worships can, if he says or does something which opens her eyes so that she sees him, not cloaked by the shimmering robe of fancy, but as he really is—a marble angel with clay feet.

"After such a shock a girl begins growing and maturing. Nor does she turn for solace to another man. Rather she devotes herself to spinning, weaving, charitable deeds, or even to building a canal.

"Samuel Talcott is a brilliant young man. He has a compelling personality. I might even have endured his drunkenness. But when, stewed to the gills, he made a laughing stock of me right before all of those Irishmen whose respect I had tried to win and hold—I just went all to pieces. To pull me out of my slump I needed to have some great demand made upon me, something that I would take very seriously. That's why I hinted that I'd like to be boss in your absence. And you, in your great heart and understanding, knew and consented."

"Sure now, Colleen, you've gone to the other extreme, giving me credit for understanding that I never had. Nor is my heart great the way you mean it. Belike someday you'll be sorry for being so outspoken to me. There's an old Irish saying. Never unburden your heart to your friends because today's friend becomes tomorrow's enemy."

Pippa shook her head. "That could have applied a year ago when I was young and confiding. Now I've grown up. While winning my struggle to get the channel dug to Seneca River before freeze-up, I have also won my struggle with myself. Two hours from now I'll be on the *Shamrock* with all of my baggage and my destination Utica. I'll spend the winter there and return to you in the spring. Meanwhile if I meet Sam Talcott on the street, my heart won't even flutter."

McShane grinned. "Sure now, maybe his will."

DeWitt Clinton

Chapter 6

MAY's POINT was a broad cape of hard soil extending southward into the vastness of Cayuga Marsh. The saw-pits which McShane's gangs had dug in the sand and gravel of the rising ground north of the cattails had a warm southern exposure. The man who stood in the pit pushing the handle of a cross-cut saw upward, while sawdust poured down into his eyes and nose, was sheltered from the wind, but the man who pushed downward from the top of a thick log was exposed to a bitter wind which caused his eyes to water and his nose to drip. At night when the other men in the warm bunk house were playing cards by candle-light and adding to the thick wreaths of tobacco smoke, the sawyers were expertly filing and setting their saws and grinding their axes to a razor-like sharpness. So strenuous was their work, they couldn't have quartered their four logs per day and sawed the squared timbers into two-inch planks had their saws been dull.

Nor could the tree cutters and trimmers have kept the sawyers supplied had they used tools any less sharp. Even the chain men were particular about bringing the big linked-iron chains into the bunk house to melt the ice accumulated on the metal and to warm the iron. Chains left out overnight sometimes snapped in the cold dawn when an undue strain was exerted on them. And a flying end could crush a man's bones as if they were egg shells. Mittens and boots also had to be kept in repair, for exposed fingers and toes usually got frostbitten, thus limiting a man's productivity and perhaps incapacitating him.

In a corner of the bunk house McShane sat at a homemade desk entering in a book each night the number of planks, stakes, and stringers cut and making an accompanying sketch of the location in the frozen marsh near the canal line where the planks had been stored on pole frames driven through ice. When the stakes were four-feet high McShane covered them with cattails until they looked like muskrat dens and houses. Indeed the sketches showed actual muskrat houses interspersed among his disguised stacks.

The evening of February 15th, 1820, McShane, having finished his bookkeeping, lit his pipe and studied a letter received that day from Pippa in which she quoted from the Albany *Argus*.

The legislature convened very early last month. It became apparent immediately that the opponents of the Canal, led by the Albany Regency, considered that the moment was favorable for introducing a measure which, if passed, and not rejected by the Council of Revision, would have been fatal to continuation of the work. They hope to stop the digging of the western division until the eastern division has been completed. The ever-increasing population which now tends to travel westward like an overflow of water seeking a new stream bed would then be dammed at Seneca River. The east would soon become thickly populated. Such a concentration of population would supply the eastern politicians with a preponderance of votes, making them all-powerful and the western politicians weak and insignificant.

The measure required appointment of a committee to inquire into the expediency of directing the Canal Commissioners . . . to delay construction of a canal west of Seneca River until the northern (Champlain) canal and the canal from Utica to the Hudson River be completed.

Governor Clinton made a speech warning the Legislature against this thinly-veiled attack upon the best interests of the State, saying "As the canal proceeds to the west, the country east will of course be accommodated. And in proportion to its progress to completion, in that ratio will it be considered easier to combine a greater mass of population against its further extension. Attempts have already been made to arrest its progress west of the Seneca River. It is highly probable that they will be renewed when the work is finished to the Genesee."

Of course a committee was appointed. They made their inquiry in the assembly and received an answer which Governor Clinton, being present, described as "The Legislators were able to comprehend the interesting truth that this State can never enjoy a tenth part of the advantages of the Erie Canal until the tide of inland commerce, of which it is to be the channel, is permitted to flow without a mile of portage from the Great Lakes to the Atlantic."

Pippa continued in her own words.

So the Legislature stands behind the Commissioners in their purpose of extending the canal from Seneca River to Lake Erie. But do not deceive yourself into believing that the Regency will allow the western division to be built if they can prevent it. What they have failed to win by guile, they may try to achieve by force.

I have heard that along the Hudson River State Banks are failing and, like a disease, failures are spreading through New England. Farmers who all their lives have scrimped and saved, putting their small savings in banks, are unable to meet payments on their mortgages. Consequently they are being dispossessed of their farms. Their wives hire out in domestic service. Their children are cast into bondage in small shops, or cleaning latrines or pigstyes on large estates. Homeless men with no means of support are tramping through the winter woods seeking employment in the construction camps cutting timbers, or stone blocks in quarries. They gladly work from dawn to dark for twenty-seven cents a day and found.

It would not be at all surprising if many of these friendless men are hired by the Regency and, having been suitably instructed, are directed to your camp, as well as to others, to destroy the planks you are cutting and to sow such discontent among your gangs, and so set them against each other, that you will neither complete your cutting of timbers nor resume digging in the spring.

Beware of new arrivals asking for work, even though you may need more men. Denny, a deserter from your camp, appeared in Utica last week drunk and proclaiming that he would strangle Talcott. Without waiting for him to fulfill his threat, Sheriff Cooper clapped him in Rome jail from which he escaped. One of the water-front characters says that he has fled to Albany.

McShane showed the letter to O'Brien and watched narrowly the little gleams and smiles which flicked across his face as he read it. After O'Brien had finished he glanced at McShane.

"If we don't hire more men we can't cut enough planks for the sheet piling. It's slow work. As the snow gets deeper, the work goes slower. Anyone who understood lumbering would know that. Sure now, whose side is she on anyway?"

McShane knocked the ashes from his pipe. "That's what I'd like to know."

"And what would you be having me do?"

"Go ahead and hire the men. Hire everybody who comes. If a man can saw or chop all day he has a job. If he can't he hasn't. We'll chance the discontent."

"Is she returning to us in the spring?"

"Aye. At least so she says."

McShane reflected. A number of ragged men had arrived lately, asking for work at any wage. He hired them at the prevailing winter rate of twenty-two and a half cents per day. They had sawed plenty of timber, but, come to think of it, they had also broken several saws. He had asked O'Brien to order more saws from Utica, but the saws had not yet arrived. McShane turned to his desk. While snores made sawing noises around him, he wrote a letter to Mr.

Devereux requesting a supply of saws, saw teeth setters, axes, files, and whetstones. He'd take the letter over to Montezuma tomorrow and dispatch it himself.

Acting on a hunch he walked to the other end of the bunk house, where the men hung their saws and piled their axes when they came clattering in. By candlelight he counted the tools. There were only half enough. Outside the trees were popping with frost. The temperature was far below zero. Unless adequately clothed it would be dangerous to step outside for even five minutes. Sacrificing men on the altar of discipline was of no interest to McShane. There were other ways of teaching them. From a tub behind a stove where snow was converted into water McShane filled a wooden bucket and set it beside bunk number two-hundred and seventeen. His book showed that it was occupied by one of the newly-arrived ragged men. McShane jerked him from his bunk, ducked his face in the bucket, stood him on his feet, held a candle lantern close to his dripping face, and asked him what he had done with his axe and saw. Bewildered, the man stammered that he couldn't remember. After hard shakes and slaps he remembered that he had left them on a stump in the cutting area.

Relaxing his grip McShane ordered him to dry his face with his blanket and to pull on his boots. Cowering, the man obeyed. In a low, hard voice McShane reminded him that he had been instructed to bring his tools back to camp each night. Looking up at him from beneath sullen brows, the man muttered insolently. McShane grabbed him with one hand, relieved him of a knife with the other, ran him down the aisle, yanked open the frost-swollen squeaking door, and shoved him stumbling into the white moonlight. McShane shouted,

"Pick up the axe and saw by the handles. If your hands

touch the cold metal, they'll stick. Run both ways. Your hands will freeze if you don't."

McShane jammed the door shut and turned to O'Brien, sitting on the edge of his bunk and rubbing his eyes. "Small wonder, O'Brien, that axe heads have been breaking and saws snapping. Deep cold crystallizes the iron and makes it brittle. Snatch all newcomers from their bunks. Let 'em pull on their boots. Then out they go, and keep going, until all the tools are inside. Then give 'em their mittens and some pack baskets and send 'em after the iron wedges. I have the tally of tools in my book. I'll count 'em as they come in. And, O'Brien, keep your eyes open for shenanigans. Some of the new arrivals have been hired in Albany and sent here to make us trouble."

As O'Brien went into action McShane hauled the cooks from their bunks. "How much flour, ham, frozen beef, coffee, and molasses have we in the larder?"

One of the cooks threw open the door of the storeroom and held a candle. McShane made a quick appraisal. "Sure, we've scarce enough to last a week. Why haven't you told me?"

The cook retorted, "Why don't the supply sleighs come? They were due eight days ago. We've been expecting them daily. They've never been late before. Of course there's been a lot of snow lately."

When the men, puffing, blowing on their numb fingers, and cursing, had stamped back into the bunk house and resumed their blankets, McShane spoke again to O'Brien.

"Come morning, go to Montezuma. Take the road southward through the woods to Seneca Turnpike. Catch the Utica Stage."

"Any expense money?"

"No. Blarney your way. Would you be remembering those bateaumen? What are they after doing in the winter?"

"Sure, J.J., they cut firewood and sell it."

"Do they own the land where they are cutting?"

"They never did. But no one was wishful of driving them off because of their mean dispositions and partly because they were getting their land cleared for nothing."

"Sure it's a fine idea to get things done for nothing. Find Mr. John Devereux and ask him to arrange it with Sheriff Apollos Cooper to arrest them for stealing trees. When they resist arrest, you appear and say that the shopkeepers would ask the owners of the land where the bateaumen are cutting to withdraw the charge if the bateaumen would do the shopkeepers a favor."

"Sure now, J.J., the shopkeepers would be the men who are sending us the sleighloads of food supplies which never reach us because the Regency highwaymen are holding up the sleighs and robbing them."

"You're getting the idea, O'Brien. Ask Mr. Devereux to send out supply sleighs some night with bateaumen instead of supplies under the tarpaulins."

O'Brien chuckled, "Sure, sure."

"And when the Regency men reach under the tarpaulins and grab the bateaumen, they'll be fighting for their lives."

"Sure, O'Brien. Have plenty of stout cord to bind the highwaymen. When they're all bound, load 'em into one sleigh and whack each highwayman on the head until he's out. Cover them over with the tarpaulin. Send the other sleigh back to Utica with a bateauman where they will be pardoned and maybe receive a few jugs. Next morning that sleigh and maybe another will be sent here with the provisions."

"And the highwaymen?"

"Ride along with them, O'Brien. Every two hours stop the sleigh and whack each one on the head again to keep 'em out until they get here. I'll cut 'em loose and pair 'em off for sawing with some mean characters we have. Those Regency men will saw up a lot of wood at no wages."

O'Brien looked doubtful. "J.J., isn't there a law about kidnapping?"

"There's nothing in the book that says it's a crime to steal a thief. Be off with you."

* * * *

In the spring McShane resumed the digging by connecting Canandaigua Outlet with the canal line at Melvin Brook. As far west as Melvin Brook the Outlet and the canal line were only a few hundred feet apart. At Melvin Brook the Outlet bore off southwestward toward Canandaigua Lake. The canal line ran along the rising ground at the edges of long, narrow swamps which divided rolling hills.

When McShane had opened a channel two miles beyond where Melvin Brook had crossed the canal line he sent back a gang to construct a temporary lock of timbers between Canandaigua Outlet and the canal channel. While the lock was being built he erected a coffer dam in the channel and continued westward. When the lock was finished, the gaps left in the tow path and berm where Melvin Brook crossed the channel were closed. A big iron pipe under the tow path admitted the brook to the channel. Three days later when two miles of the channel were half-filled with water the *Shamrock* passed through the lock from the Outlet and floated up to the coffer dam with a load of supplies and Benjamin Wright.

Wright's face brightened when he saw McShane. The weather was cool but Wright was mopping sweat with a damp bandana and fanning his neck with his hat. McShane looked at him askance.

"Sure, by the looks of your hat, I thought it was for swatting flies rather than a covering to conceal your lack of hair."

Wright smiled faintly. "I am concerned, McShane. Contractors, starting at Rochester, have been digging southward

and eastward. They've cut a prism of proper dimensions
and angles, and they've built a fine stone aqueduct. They've
passed Pittsford and reached Irondequoit Valley, where the
canal line makes a half ellipse coming down the west bank,
crossing on some drumlins and curving up the east bank.
However, the spaces between the drumlins must be filled
with earth to form an embankment. The distance is two
miles, and the depth is sixty-five feet. Where Irondequoit
Creek runs through the embankment we must also build a
thirty-five-foot high stone arch with bases resting on quicksand. The drumlins and all nearby earth are sand and gravel,
and porous as cloth."

Wright glanced covertly at McShane. "Do you think you
can lick that?"

"Sure. It's hardly a problem. What else is the matter?"

Wright's expression was incredulous, but he continued.
"Eastward at Herkimer on the south bank of the Mohawk
River the channel has been cut through the base of a hill
of breccia which slopes into the river. When the breccia is
softened by rain it slides into the channel and blocks it.
The engineers can't stop it. Can you?"

McShane grunted, "Sure. With one hand. How soon do
we start?"

"Huh? Er—how would you go about doing it?"

"If I should be telling you, you still couldn't do it
yourself."

"What makes you say that?"

In a tone of asperity McShane answered, "Only the Irish
can do it, but they won't do it unless properly bossed. If
you kow tow to them, they'll walk all over you. If you
holler at them, they'll fight you. If you use force, they'll
kill you."

"Then how do you boss them?"

McShane spoke impatiently, "I'm after saying that even
if I should tell you, you couldn't do it. Instead of question-

ing me, tell me what you want done. If I can't do it, I'll
say so. What's your next problem?"

Wright scowled. McShane started to walk away. Wright
called him back.

"Welsh masons have been hired to blast a canal channel
at Little Falls, a mile-long groove in the cliff on the south
side of the river. And after the blasting has been finished
it will take three years to build a stone-block wall wide
enough for the tow path and high enough to contain the
channel."

"Of course. Work is hard to find except the building of
the canal. The masons want the job. They'll stretch it to
three years if you'll let 'em. The wall with a lock at the
east end can be built this year."

"You can do that?"

"You said the masons were Welsh."

"Yes. Oneida County Welsh. Mostly from Utica."

"Welsh are rabbits to a man who bosses the Irish."

"McShane, you're pretty sure of yourself for all these
promises."

"The only thing I'm not sure of is when you'll stop talking and start eastward."

*　　*　　*　　*

Wright and McShane traveled eastward in a bateau
poled rapidly along the canal by two burly men who had
been bateaumen on the Mohawk River a few years before.
On their way to Herkimer they passed many bateaux skim-
ming both ways. The boat men were picking up fares in
the manner of cab drivers in city streets.

Passing south of Herkimer on the fourth day, they still
had enough light to see the unstable hillside of breccia and
the gaunt frame of a pile driver, lonely against the evening
sky. At the base the hill was studded with piles. Mud had
oozed between them and over into the canal. The channel

BENJAMIN WRIGHT

had been choked to such an extent that it scraped the bottom of the bateau. Wright explained.

"A gang of men comes in here every morning with shovels and buckets and opens the ditch enough so that boats can squeeze through, if the drivers hitch on another team of horses. But we can't keep men working here indefinitely. Now, what is your solution?"

"Well, Engineer Wright, you shouldn't have cut into that hill in the first place. However, breccia can be held in place by planting grass and bushes."

"But how can we stop it now?"

"You can't. That hill will fill the canal ditch level. After that the mud and pebbles will flow east and west along the ditch until it has filled about two hundred feet of the channel. If you should dig it out, it would fill right up again."

"Then we'll have to take down the hill."

"It's a big hill. In dry weather that clay will bake in the sun as hard as soft slate."

"You've had experience with breccia?"

"Aye."

"Then what do you propose?"

"Go round it. Drive piles along the water's edge in a line that will straighten the indents of the bank. Nail panels of planks to the piles. Because clay just above the river edge is firmed by erosion of the current, the pressure of breccia flowing from the hill won't make the bank bulge. Some breccia will slide across the tow path you've already built and move down over the bank into the water, until it fills the open space between the bank and the row of piles which I have suggested be driven a yard or so out from shore. The new tow path will be in the river another fifty feet out. To build it you begin at the bank a little distance up-river and set sheet piling in the water in a crescent, returning to shore just below the hill. Pump out the water enclosed by the crescent and shovel out the mud, making a ten-foot ditch along the sheet piling. Dig down to ledge rock. Chisel out the rock to a depth of six inches for the full ten-foot width and make it level. Then using cement and blocks build a solid stone wall ten-feet wide. That will be the tow path. Then admit water to the new channel as soon as you have connected it with the old channel above and below the hill. A plain iron railing on the river side of the new tow path of stone would prevent teams from falling into the river."

Wright murmured, "Build the canal out into the river?" In a louder tone he asked, "What will happen to the stone wall when the spring flood strikes it with ice floes forty-feet wide and two-feet thick?"

"Sure 'twill be like a haymaker punch. You take it on the top or side of your head. 'Tis a glancing blow and never does any harm."

"But won't the flood come over the stone wall and wash out the berm?"

"Not if the wall is built high enough."

"Well, let's all go ashore and find accommodations for the night. We'll push on to Little Falls in the morning."

• • • • •

The Mohawk River tumbled down stairs at Little Falls. Passing between rising slopes which became a hill on the north and a crumbling cliff on the south, the river allowed no space for the canal. Welsh miners, employed by the Canal Commissioners, had blasted a groove in the cliff face from the western to the eastern end. The cliff projected and receded. The groove was straight where possible, but there were several curves. As Wright and McShane followed them next day, picking their way over blasted rubble, McShane remarked on the accuracy of the blasting. From a pile of scrap lumber McShane had picked up a straight stick.

Every hundred steps he stopped, pulled away big chunks and small fragments of rock, and laid his stick on the rock floor. Going down on his knees he squinted at the contact length of the stick. It was always level.

At the eastern end McShane turned, looked back, and gave his verdict. "I never cared for the Welsh, but I admit that they know how to blast rock. Let's find their boss."

The boss, a burly, noisy Welshman named Jones ap Kerig, was too busy to talk to them. While Wright and McShane stood watching he bullied his men with sarcasm and insulting remarks, raising his voice to reach the more distant. The men, obviously fearful of losing their jobs, cowered under the tongue-lashing.

In disgust McShane turned to Wright. "Sure he's blasted a good bed for the canal, but at the rate his men are cutting the stone into blocks for the retaining wall they won't live long enough to finish it."

Wright hesitated. "I'm aware of that, but he's the only one we know of who could blast a channel through that cliff. To get him we had to give him a contract for the complete job without a time limit. And he is paid by the day. Now, we'd like to get rid of him. David Bates, the lock builder, would be the man to finish the job. He's fine for locks and walls but not much of a disciplinarian. Your Tom Mooney would be fine for that."

"Sure, but I could do it better."

Joy and relief lighted Wright's square face. "You would?"

"If you could assure me of a contract to build Irondequoit Embankment and channel, another to build Genesee River Aqueduct, and another for the first two sections of Tonawanda Ridge, I might."

Wright's expression became pensive. He muttered, "I jumped for the bait."

After consideration he continued, "Would you be willing

to accept just a contract for the Irondequoit, stipulating no payment until the embankment had been tried and found operable?"

McShane considered. "Say one-half at the regular rate of payment, the balance after a boat goes across the embankment. I'll start the work moving here at Little Falls, then I'll turn it over to Mooney and Donohue."

"Very well. I'll do all I can to have it written as you wish. And Mooney and Donohue will be satisfactory. Now what about Jones ap Kerig?"

"Introduce me to him as a stone mason looking for a job. I'll take it from there. When this lock and wall are finished and I return to my men, I'll be taking Jones with me. I can use him."

"Of his own free will?"

"He will have the free use of his hands and feet."

"Sufficient. Come along and meet Jones."

At the introduction McShane hung his head, turned his hat between his fingers, and whined for a job. He knew that Jones was studying him closely, but he did not look up.

Jones shouted to a foreman to give McShane a mallet and chisel, slapped his big red hand against McShane's back, and gave him a shove that made him stumble. With drooping shoulders McShane hurried to the foreman, received his tools, knelt beside a jagged chunk of stone, and began chipping.

An hour later Jones, bawling insults at the foreman, passed McShane and paused long enough to kick him viciously in the pants.

"You dirty whelp of an Irishman! When I come by, you stand up."

Slowly and with apparent difficulty McShane arose, keeping his weight on his right foot. Pivoting on his left, he swung a hard right uppercut to Jones' chin. Jones' head flew back with a snap of dislocated bones. Shifting his weight McShane sent a haymaker into Jones' midriff. As Jones doubled over, McShane's clasped hands came up in a lift-punch which sent Jones sprawling backward. McShane raised Jones by an ear and beat the man's face with his opened right hand. Then he dragged the unconscious Jones to the stone which he had been chipping, flung him down, sat on him, and continued his chipping. Glancing at the astonished foreman McShane explained,

"I always find it comfortable in April to sit on something while I work. The ground hasn't warmed up yet."

Wright, on his way to the bateau, had spoken to a foreman named Perley Harris. Harris now came forward, cupped his hands, and shouted that Engineer Wright's parting orders were that if Jones ap Kerig should become incapacitated, regardless of the reason, the McShane was to take his place, and they were all to take orders from the McShane until ap Kerig was able to resume his duties. Harris walked over to McShane and said,

"Sir, what are your orders?"

"Clear the canal bed of rubble. Forty feet from the cliff chisel a true level twelve-feet wide to be the base of the wall, perpendicular on the outside, eighty-degree angle inside, rising to flat top ten-feet wide with an outside coping one-foot wide and three-feet high. Build the wall of squared stone blocks.

"I only ask that each man cut as many stone blocks in a day as I do. More if he can. Sand and cement will come down from Utica by boat. By the time it arrives I expect you to be ready to start laying and cementing. Six weeks will be allowed. The following six weeks you'll build a three-arch stone aqueduct to carry a feeder from the north bank across the river. The canal will need plenty of water at this point to fill the locks which David Bates will build at the east end of the cliff. Foreman take charge!"

Immediately the scene became a swarming of organized

activity. Beneath him McShane felt Jones stirring and tapped his head with the mallet to quiet him.

Inevitably there were noisy arguments down the line. McShane arose from his comfortable seat on Jones' back and walked composedly from group to group, resolving their difficulties with an explanation or a just word. Rarely did he use a threat.

Returning in the afternoon he found Jones playing "duck on a rock" with some boys who had earlier brought their fathers basket-lunches. Jones seemed to be enjoying the game and the boys. Although not winning he was trying hard. McShane summoned a doctor. The doctor knew Jones well and was as shocked as McShane at his sudden interest in boys' games. While they watched, one of the boys caught Jones cheating. Whereupon all of the boys threw away their "ducks" and went home, leaving Jones sitting on the ground sulking.

McShane demanded, "What ails him, Doctor?"

The doctor shrugged. "Someone has knocked him foolish. Ap Kerig is normally a man of choleric humor. A severe blow on his neck has produced a hiatus which has temporarily changed his humor to sanguine. This compels his mind to run back through memory to a time when he was naturally sanguine, namely his boyhood. Apprehended in one of his boyhood failings by other boys, he relapses into the melancholic humor. It's likely to continue until someone asks him to play a game, run a race, or go fishing."

"Sure now, Doctor, this is interesting. But when will that red-headed Welshman grow up again?"

"Who can say? The long step is from the sanguine back to the choleric. But what's the hurry? I'd say he'll be easier to get along with the way he is."

"Sure it must be as you say. But what could bring him back?"

"Another equally-hard knock on the neck from the opposite side. But it's like a man who whittles a stick. Can the man whittle another exactly like it? Or one entirely different in every particular?"

"Then what's to become of him? If he stays here, his family will have just another boy and no one at the head. When word goes around that he purposely delayed construction he'll lose his reputation with his neighbors."

"D'ye mean he's sold out to the Regency?"

"I have no proof of that, sir. Form your own conclusions. This construction will be finished by autumn. Before my men leave, one of them will give ap Kerig a left uppercut which should restore him."

The doctor sniffed, "Heroic treatment, but it may work."

* ❄ * ❄

McShane's bid for a contract to build an embankment across Irondequoit Valley was priced at twenty-five cents per cubic yard of earth supplied. He had never seen the Irondequoit. As the days passed he became more and more convinced that his bid might prove ruinously low. Therefore he was relieved to learn in a letter from Wright that the Staff of State Engineers had rejected his bid because the available soil, including the drumlins, where the canal line crossed the Irondequoit was mostly sand and gravel and obviously too porous to hold water. Also his price was too high. McShane resolved to turn the management of his men over to O'Brien and visit the three sections he had wished to build. Under O'Brien his men might not make such progress in digging the channel, but to know what lay to the westward was more important at the moment.

McShane mounted his horse and, following the canal line, rode to Irondequoit Valley. He found the soil porous and the banks of the stream lined with quicksand. For centuries a prehistoric northward-flowing stream had flooded the valley and washed the sand about until the grains had been chafed into tiny spheroids which for lack of cohesive irregular edges would not support any weight: quicksand. Finding a spot where he could cross, McShane roamed westward until he met a Pittsford farmer who guided him to a bed of blue clay. After the embankment had been built, the channel across the top could be puddled, that is, lined, with a three-inch thickness of blue clay. It would make a navigable trough, and although the deep frost of winter might crack it, it could be repaired.

Farther on where the canal line crossed the Genesee River at Rochester the river bed was flat limestone ledge. McShane left his horse with a blacksmith for shoeing and walked down the river bed, left mostly dry by the summer-shrunken current. The bed was mainly gray dolomite, but two or three miles downstream, in glancing at the high, rocky bank he saw a broad layer of red sandstone obtruding. A dull red streak in the ledge of the eastern bank indicated that the vein ran east and west and had been pierced in prehistoric times by the Genesee River.

McShane climbed the west bank. For several miles westward the forest had been pushed back. He saw farms and grazing cattle. Toward the southwest he could distinguish with a pocket field glass the rows of peeled stakes marking the canal line. Their direction inclined to the northwest. Somewhere out there the red sandstone lay under perhaps six feet of earth but close to the peeled pegs.

By digging out that section of the canal channel, feeding its short length from one of two available brooks, the dug-out channel could be filled to a depth of four feet. A flatboat could be knocked together and loaded with red sandstone blocks quarried from a few yards away. A team of horses could haul the boat to the intersection of the channel with the west bank of the Genesee River. A wooden chute could be erected so that the blocks could be slid down to the flat rock of the dry bed. Then the erection of the largest and most beautiful stone arch aqueduct in the new world could be started. Of all available stone only red sandstone could withstand the current of a stream like the Genesee during high water.

McShane returned, paid the blacksmith, bought a bag of oats for the horse, and rode westward to the foot of Mountain Ridge.* The country was waterless and, excepting a few deep, wide ravines, level. One ravine, Sandy Creek, was much deeper than Irondequoit. In a saddlebag he had a pen-and-ink copy of a surveyor's map of Tonawanda Summit (also known as Mountain Ridge) and the adjacent country which included a swamp through which both Oak Orchard and Tonawanda creeks flowed. At one point they were only a mile apart. He had copied the map from a survey made by David Thomas.

The map showed a rise of sixty feet from the foot of the ridge to the leveling at the brow and from there, for a mile and a half, a gradual ascent of thirty vertical feet to the peak of the ridge. Five pairs of twelve-foot locks were indicated, each of standard length and width so that boats going westward could rise upstairs while eastbound boats were dropping downstairs. The floor of each lock chamber was designed to a depth where a boat of standard size with a maximum load would clear the locksill of the next lock above or below. All lock chambers would have to be hewn from solid rock and afterward smoothed with cement like plastering a wall. And the rock was dolomite.

McShane tied his horse to a tree, lit his clay pipe, and sat down to reflect. The engineers expected the contractors to cut a channel through that mass of solid rock. How? And with what? From experience McShane knew that can-

* Lockport.

non powder, although stronger than musket powder, was nevertheless woefully weak, perhaps a force of six hundred pounds to the square inch. The alternative would be to drill a row of one-inch holes a foot back from the edge of the ledge, heat the stone with a wood fire, pour cold water on it, then break it off with a sledge. That method would be incredibly slow. On the other hand cannon powder, which was sold in twenty-five pound kegs, would be very expensive because of the high cost of transportation from New York City or Massachusetts. Also, the Irish disregard for danger would result in accidents. He would base his bid price on the cost of an estimated quantity of powder and try to think of some less expensive, but more efficient, method. As for the estimated quantity of powder—?

McShane studied the sketch. From where he sat it was seven miles over the top and down the southwestern slope to the end of the rock. From there to the fork in Tonawanda Creek the channel would be cut through wet earth. The surrounding area abounded in swamps. McShane wondered why Thomas had specified such a deep cut through Mountain Ridge until he noticed that the finished floor of the canal channel would be four-feet lower than the summer surface of Lake Erie. This would provide abundant water not only for the five pairs of locks, but for the sixty-mile stretch of dry country between Mountain Ridge and the Genesee River.

The sketch also showed that Thomas had made borings to determine the depth of the soil above the substratum of rock. Beginning at the eastern side and passing over the Ridge for two miles the solid rock was nowhere less than two feet from the surface. Beyond that it varied, but no boring showed the earth mat over the rock to be less than six feet. At Tonawanda Creek the cutting would have to be to a depth of twelve feet.

Because the floor of the channel from the northerly fork

of Tonawanda Creek must slope eastward, all of the water in the swamps would drain eastward into the channel while the men were trying to dig westward. If those swamps were supplied by springs, the excavators would be creating the bed of a new brook which would engulf them while they worked. There was even a good chance of breaking into subterranean streams as they cut down through bedrock. Also, when they cut into bedrock they would have to erect a retaining wall of thick stone blocks on each side to hold back the earth.

Shaking his head, McShane walked back over the Ridge, pausing frequently to look again and reflect. He was still pondering when he mounted and retraced the route eastward to his men. On his way he paused frequently to draw sketches and jot information, measurements, and possibilities in his notebook. Some of the obstacles seemed, even to him, insurmountable.

Four evenings later McShane rode into Lyons. At their normal rate of digging his men should have been there, but there was no sign of them. Apprehensive, McShane rode on in the dark towering forest. Peeled stakes in patches of moonlight kept him on his course. The canal line made a double curve, easward, north, then again eastward. He emerged on flat swampy land.

Two miles from Melvin Brook McShane rode into the cleared canal line, which adjoined a long narrow pond from which moon mist was rising. He forced his horse up on the half-finished tow path for a look around. The men had made an excavation, and swamp water had drained into it. Obviously, O'Brien had been baffled and unable to discharge the water. So all work had stopped.

At the eastern end of the narrow pond McShane saw rows of bark cylinders in which the men were probably sleeping, each end stuffed with dead leaves or pine needles to keep out mosquitoes. Nearby there was a white tent with

"PIPPA" scrawled on the canvas in charcoal. In a low, firm voice he called, "Pippa come out here."

In about the length of time it would take a frontier girl to pull on her boots, Pippa popped through the tent flap and ran to meet him, tucking her flannel shirt under the waistband of her short skirt. Beside his horse she paused, buckling on a broad black belt. Looking down at her, McShane fixed his attention on the moonbeams reflected from her thick, naturally-wavy yellow hair. She had tied it back with a short rawhide thong. It seemed to him that such hair deserved a bit of ribbon. Bending low in the saddle he extended his hand. She clasped it between both of hers, stood on her right leg, planted her left foot against the horse's flank, and gave a sudden quick pull.

Taken by surprise, and off balance, McShane had only time to kick his feet free of the iron stirrups. He did a flying mare, turning over in the air, and landed on his back with a whack that knocked the wind out of his lungs. Still clasping his hand between hers, Pippa sat on his chest exclaiming, "You are overdoing, and I'll bet that's the first time you've been out of the saddle today. You have no idea how glad I am to see you. Things here have been going at sixes and sevens. Hush! You are making a noise like the dying groan of a Scotch bagpipe." She clapped a hand over his mouth. "Stop it. You'll arouse the men. My words are confidential."

McShane gasped, "Sure, I think my back is broken."

Pippa turned him half over, ran a finger down his spine, and scolded, "Your back is all right. A few ribs might be floating, but they'll soon come ashore. Now listen. O'Brien knows how to handle the men. He has the blarney. But he doesn't know how to solve even the simplest engineering problems. When the men come to something that they can't do, like draining this pond, O'Brien can't do it either. So when Donohue sent a letter here a few days ago asking

for a few men to come and help him lick the Welsh at
Little Falls, most of the men went. A few remained. They've
been drunk and useless ever since."

"Why didn't you try to stop so many from going to
Little Falls? Sure you must have known I'd be returning
soon."

"No such thing. And now that you are here, and I've
got you anchored, you've got to listen to me. I could have
stopped a lot of those men from going. I didn't because I
learned in Utica that Talcott, through his agents, has been
trying to persuade the people at Little Falls that the canal
will deprive them of their revenue from carrying cargoes
and bateaux on the one-mile portage around the Falls. He
tells them to use every legal means and big and little
annoyances—like stirring the Welsh against the Irish and
the other way round."

McShane shifted Pippa from his chest to his stomach.
"The Irish and the Welsh brawl is of little importance. The
Irish will see to it. But a community duly organized and
established under statutory law has certain civil rights
which if exercised might hold up canal construction within
their corporate limits until the State Supreme Court, or
belike the legislature, could overrule them. We can endure
fever, fights, freezing, snow, rain, hunger, and exhaustion.
We can find ways to solve the problems of nature. But,
we can't contend with the law, and Talcott is a smart,
unscrupulous lawyer."

Pippa considered. "You should go to Little Falls yourself, J.J."

"Agreed, but who's to get the work started here?"

"I will, if you authorize me."

"How would you be draining the water from this section?"

"I'd close the gates of all the feeder brooks to stop the
water from pouring into the channel. Then I'd open the

lock at Jordan and let the water flow eastward until these swamps were dry. Then I'd resume excavation until well past this condition. After that I'd close the lock at Jordan and open the feeder gates."

Pippa sprang to her feet and held out her hands to help him up. "How's that?"

McShane, ignoring her hands, arose without assistance. "It's all right. I'll tell O'Brien that I've made you straw boss. The authority will be his, but he's to be guided by you."

Pippa clapped her hands. "Wonderful! It's more than I'd hoped for."

Suddenly the frogs stopped croaking. Insects stopped scraping and chirping. McShane's horse reared and whinnied. From the blackness of the forest came the sharp scream of a panther.

McShane looked doubtfully at Pippa.

She shrugged. "Oh that old thing. Worst nuisance. It comes snuffling around here every night looking for garbage. All you have to do is throw a stick at it. You'll find O'Brien in the first bark cylinder. Holler to him as you approach so that he won't throw something at you, mistaking you for the panther. The last cylinder is empty. You can sleep there."

McShane swung into the saddle. "Sure I'd like to, but I must get to Little Falls—and probably no sleep after I get there. Good-bye, Colleen. I'm grateful for your loyalty."

NATHAN ROBERTS

Chapter 7

AT JORDAN, where McShane stopped for breakfast after riding all night, he learned of the horrors of the Cayuga Marsh. The contractors who had bid successfully for sections in that vast expanse of waving cattails were not experienced canal engineers. They were farmers, storekeepers, or lawyers who had believed that by hiring Irish immigrants on the docks of New York City— at well below prevailing canal wages—they could make a big profit since digging a forty-foot-wide ditch through a swamp would be easy.

It was. But the ditch wouldn't stay dug. The weight of the mud the diggers piled on the banks pressed the mud beneath until it squeezed out into the channel and filled it. Not one of the contractors had thought to sink sheet piling for siding as they cut the ditch through the marsh.

McShane's first impulse was to hasten to the marsh and tell them. However, he was advised to deviate to the Seneca Turnpike by the shortest route possible, for the Cayuga Marsh from the Mead farm for eleven miles southeast around May's Point and up to Seneca River Crossing at Montezuma was alive with swamp fever. Hundreds of Irishmen had died from it. Hundreds more were prostrate in temporary bunk houses with no one to feed them or bring them a drink of water. Scores had quit and had tried to find their way out of the marsh. Many had lost their way and had not been heard of. The contractors themselves were dead or dying. To enter that swamp would be courting death under a blazing, pitiless sun.

Because there was nothing he could have done, or could do now, to avert such a disaster McShane sought the turnpike. His heart was heavy. Back of it lay the question of what effect this would have on Governor Clinton and the canal cause; and how Talcott would use it to turn people against the canal?

When the reply came to his mind, it also answered another question. What of the Irish immigrants who had worked afield from dawn until dark, who had plowed all day in the driving rain of winter to earn a few extra shillings, the ingenious, industrious men of ambition who had come to America, eager to learn, eager to advance themselves by labor, and alert for opportunity. They had proven their sincerity and courage and had been absorbed by that deadly swamp. So for their sakes as well as for Governor Clinton and the canal cause, the canal must be built.

When McShane reached Little Falls his eyes looked as if they were peering through burned holes in a blanket. He was faint from hunger, but without either food or rest he set about driving his men as well as the Welsh. Mooney and Donahue had coordinated the labor effort fairly well, but McShane converted them into a big machine of many parts. The Welsh had blasted a mile-long hollow in the face of the cliff. McShane erected a high retaining wall of cemented stone blocks, broad at the base and narrowing to a width of ten feet at the top. That was the tow path. A plain iron railing protected the horses from falling into the river, which swirled all along the base of the wall.

In the fall, after completing the standard-width channel of the canal, two eastward locks, and a feeder which brought water from the north side of the river on a stone three-arch aqueduct, McShane made a brief speech to the assembled Irish and Welsh. As a tribute to the brave Irishmen who had been killed by the Cayuga Marsh that summer, he had resolved to cut an eleven-mile channel through during the coming winter. Would they spend that winter standing in the icy water and muddy snow when they could be at home sitting near the fireplace? Cold and weary or warm and comfortable? Before he had finished talking they all shouted agreement. The Welsh insisted that they be allowed to lead the march westward. Exchanging winks, the Irish consented to Welsh leadership alternate days. McShane, who had expected to lead, walked last with head bowed in thankful humility. He was deeply proud of his men.

All the tools and equipment had been sent in small boats up the canal to Montezuma, Seneca River, and Canandaigua Outlet as far as the confluence of Black Brook, and a quarter of a mile beyond. From there it was only a hundred yards across the swamp to Crusoe's Island a bit above May's Point. Using the abundance of trees on Crusoe's Island a causeway would have to be built across the narrow stretch of marsh to the hard ground of the island. There being no other transportation available, the men walked, each man carrying his baggage tied up in a handkerchief on the end of a stick. Tom Mooney temporarily lamed by an accident rode McShane's horse.

Snow was falling when they reached Montezuma. The boatmen, having built the causeway and discharged the freight, had come to Montezuma on their way home. Ignoring their bitter complaints, McShane ordered the boatmen to transport his men to the causeway. When they began to argue vociferously about an infringement of their rights, the boatmen mysteriously ended in the water.

As the last of the boats was poled westward leaving a group of raving, gesticulating boatmen standing hip-deep in the icy water, two boats, nailed together, were poled in by a powerful apple-cheeked young man. He stepped ashore, nodded to McShane, and said,

"I'm John Littlejohn, Jr., from Fort Hunter. I've heard a lot about you, Mr. McShane, and I need your help. I have a contract to build a dam there across Schoharie Creek six-hundred-and-fifty-feet long and eight-feet high. I've driven four rows of piles in the stream bed with two-foot spacing between the rows."

McShane looked him up and down with some astonishment. "And how many feet between piles in each row?"

"Four. And, using the piles as fence posts, I've made each row a sort of board fence by spiking on planks of two-inch thickness. I filled the spaces between the fences with creek-bed stones, and I did most of it during summer low water."

"Did you continue driving piles at each end well up on the bank?"

"Yes. And there they are like the ends of a long rope. I'd like to tie them to something to have an anchor for the dam on each bank."

"A good thought, young man. And quite necessary. How will you do it?"

"I don't know. Another thing: What can I do to keep the ice from tearing out the work I've done when it comes down with the spring freshet? Look, Mr. McShane. In my two boats nailed together I have four rectangles of iron, all of the same size, four-inches thick, each weighing one hundred pounds, and each fitted with a ring bolt at one end. The ring is in the exact center, which I found by scratching a letter X with a straight rule from corner to corner. There's a ratchet, a pulley, and a greased rope that goes with each. I used them in wooden frames eighteen-feet high for trip hammers to drive my piles. Mr. Henry Hill made them for me. I paid for them, and they're yours if you'll tell me how to save my dam from the ice."

"Sure now, lad, I'll tell you the best I know how, and I'll go with you to help you build an ice shield. I've had but little experience with fast rivers and ice, but I've seen the Mohawk River in spring. So I've an idea. And thank you for the pile drivers. I was about to have my men hammer the tongued and grooved planks into the frozen mud with sledges while they stood on platforms, but your trip hammers will be so much better."

"I'll have no further use for them unless my dam lets go. Isn't there something I can do around my dam while I'm waiting for you to come?"

"Sure now, there is. Grease your boots. With rakes and potato hooks drag the stones in the creek bed on the upstream side from the ends of your dam towards the center of your channel until you've made the stream bed fairly level above your dam from bank to bank for a distance of thirty feet upstream. Start two feet upstream from your row of piles, and half-way between piles, and grub parallel ditches in the stream bed heading upstream the full length of your cleared space, keeping them four feet apart. Fill each ditch with a thick log. Then five feet from the upstream ends lay logs across the bottom logs at four-foot intervals back to the lower ends. On them lay twenty-foot logs pointed upstream. Come back five feet and lay that same pattern of crosswise logs. Spike or peg all logs together and fill the spaces between with stones.

"When finished you'll have a shelving crib with five-foot steps from the smoothed stream bed to the top of your pile dam. Then spike down four-inch seasoned planks from your dam right down those steps to the bottom so that your crib will have a sloping roof or shield.

"The ends of the planks should project far enough to join a plank roof spiked down over the tops of the piles. The downstream side of the roof must extend far enough to drop the current on a stepped cribwork apron to prevent washing out below the dam. Thick ice drifting downstream will impact on your upstream shield and slide up and over the dam carried by the force of the current.

"Would you like me to draw you a diagram?"

"That won't be necessary, Mr. McShane. I understand what you've said."

"Well now, it's a bright lad you are. I might as well tell you about the anchors. Dig into each bank at the end of your dam. At water edge open a five-foot space either side of your piles two feet deep and eighteen feet back into the banks. Lay a mat of foot-square timbers and another on top crisscross. Spike them all together. Then build an abutment of stone blocks on each mat in such a way that the end piles of your dam are incorporated deep in the abutments. Cement the stone blocks together.

"Then let the Schoharie rise in all its fury. You'll see ice fields and floating trees slide over the roof of your dam without even slowing down."

"There'll be plenty of fury in the spring, Mr. McShane. The Schoharie Creek drains a thousand square miles of hills and mountains. I don't know if I can get all that stream bed levelled off when ice is forming along the edges, and then set all those logs and nail down the planks, even though I work all winter."

Smiling, McShane clapped him on the shoulder. "Despite the obstacles, lad, if you haven't done it complete by spring, all that you have done so far will go down the river. If you have any Irish blood in you, you'll get it done somehow. If you haven't, you won't. Now, have you any Irish blood?"

"Not that I know of."

McShane shook his head, then suddenly brightened. "It was kind of you to bring me those pile drivers. I'm leaving my horse here. I'll join you in your boats. At Crusoe's Island we'll unload the hardware, and you may pick up my foreman James O'Brien to spend the winter with you. He couldn't build a doghouse, but he'll find labor for you and he'll make them work. But you must handle him right, or

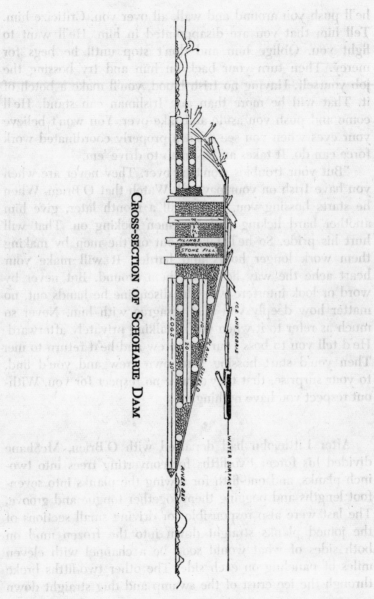

CROSS-SECTION OF SCHOHARIE DAM

he'll push you around and walk all over you. Criticize him. Tell him that you are disappointed in him. He'll want to fight you. Oblige him and don't stop until he begs for mercy. Then turn your back on him and try bossing the job yourself. Having no Irish blood, you'll make a botch of it. That will be more than any Irishman can stand. He'll come and push you aside and take over. You won't believe your eyes when you see what a properly coordinated work force can do. It takes an Irishman to drive 'em.

"But your troubles won't be over. They never are when you have Irish on your pay roll. Watch that O'Brien. When he starts bossing you, as he will a month later, give him another hard licking with the men looking on. That will hurt his pride. So he'll take it out on the men by making them work longer hours and harder. It will make your heart ache the way he'll cuff them around. But never by word or look interfere with the discipline he hands out, no matter how deeply you may disagree with him. Never so much as refer to it when you're talking privately afterward. He'd tell you to boss your own crew and he'd return to me. Then you'd start bossing your own crew and you'd find, to your surprise, that they'd have no respect for you. Without respect you have nothing."

❖ ❖ ❖ ❖

After Littlejohn had departed with O'Brien, McShane divided his force: two-fifths for converting trees into two-inch planks, and one-fifth for sawing the planks into seven-foot lengths and pegging them together tongue and groove. The last were also responsible for driving small sections of the joined planks straight down into the frozen mud on both sides of what would soon be a channel with eleven miles of paneling on each side. The other two-fifths broke through the ice crust of the swamp and dug straight down and across between the panels. Branches, bark, scrap wood, and twigs were mixed with the mud in the tow path. Two gravel pits were opened on the slopes of May's Point and thawed by wood fires so that the gravel could be spread on soft spots.

Except for a few days, when the weather would not permit, the Irish worked at a frenzied pitch. McShane never missed an opportunity to remind them that the souls of the Irishmen who had died in that marsh the preceding summer were watching from above.

*   *   *   *

By late Spring of 1822 the channel had been completed across Cayuga Marsh, with a guard lock installed at the eastern end to keep the Seneca River from backing into the canal and overflowing it during high water.

That portion of his force which McShane had left the previous summer to be guided and bossed by Pippa and O'Brien had cut the channel to Hartwell's Basin bordering on the Irondequoit Valley.

Pippa had hired farmers in the Basin on the eastern side of the valley, and at Pittsford on the western side, to haul dirt during their spare time and dump it into the spaces between drumlins, like building up between giant steppingstones. O'Brien had built two bunk houses and a cook shack near where the channel ended, and this would remain the end until the huge embankment had been built across the mile-wide valley. He told McShane that the channel would be sixty-five feet above the valley floor, and that a stone arch twenty-five-feet high, thirty-feet wide and a hundred-feet long must be built to pass Irondequoit Brook beneath the embankment. On either side the bases of the arch would have to rest on quicksand.

McShane, as he listened to O'Brien's story, had shaken

his head at his own estimate that it might require a thousand twenty-foot logs pile-driven and overlaid with mats of timber and grouting to provide foundations for the bases of that stone arch.

＊　　＊　　＊　　＊

With the spring thaw and cold rains of 1822, the tow path across the Cayuga Marsh became impassable. The sheet piling on both sides of the channel, swollen tight by moisture, prevented water in the tow path from seeping into the canal although the water surface was more than a foot below. To provide a firm surface for the tow path McShane ordered hemlock trees of one-foot diameter to be felled, trimmed, and split lengthwise. These were laid on the tow path lengthwise, end to end, parallel and ten feet apart, flat side down. Crosspieces were spiked at intervals to hold them in place. Enough mud squeezed up between the half logs to level the rounded bark surface.

The tow path was still unfinished when word came that the *Shamrock* had arrived at Montezuma from Utica with a full load of food supplies and Pippa with her tent, baggage, and no donkey.

McShane sent back an order to have the draft horses driven over the road through Savannah to Clyde while the *Shamrock* was being poled to May's Point. All boats immediately following the *Shamrock* must also be poled and must stop at May's.

As fast as boats arrived McShane filled them with men and sent them on to Hartwell's Basin. When the *Shamrock* came, Pippa, standing on the gunwale, waved to McShane. Without ceasing to give orders to the men crowding on the dock and to the men in the small boats who didn't want to take extra passengers, McShane waved back. Pippa sprang ashore and caught McShane's arm between her hands.

"Hello, J.J., I'm glad to see you again. And you?"

"Sure, Colleen, I'm glad to see the first flower after a long, cold winter in this gray and dreary waste. You're like having the sun come out in the late afternoon of a rainy day." Reaching out with a long boat hook, McShane stopped a small boat. "Oh no you don't. Come to the dock now and take aboard three men. If that's too many, two of you may get out in the water and push."

McShane gripped Pippa's shoulder shaking her gently. "'Tis only when you return in the spring that I know how much I've missed you. Thank you, I won't be shaking hands, for I've no mind to another spring over your head, and this time to land in the canal."

Pippa threw an arm around his neck, drawing his head close. In his ear she whispered, "To delay Littlejohn the Regency sent two troublemakers to serve in his gang. Their purpose was to persuade the workmen to lose tools through the ice and such, and in the end to strike. Then the dam wouldn't be strong enough to stand the spring flood."

McShane nodded and said aloud, "Sure. That's why I sent O'Brien."

Pippa whispered again, "It wasn't just tools that went through the ice. The troublemakers disappeared that way too. O'Brien has been jailed in Johnstown on suspicion of murder. He admits that they went downstream when they fell in, but he says that they escaped through a natural hole at the next rift. He claims that they wish to be thought dead. They have run away to escape their wives."

"That's what could be expected of the sort of men the Regency would hire." McShane straightened up. "Colleen, the work you bossed from Lyons to Hartwell's Basin was done well. I'll be going with you to Irondequoit to get the task of building a mile-long embankment started. The deep filling is between three drumlins, a stretch of some five-hundred yards. The rest is more or less evening up the natural slopes and depressions. I'll go with you and show what I want done. Will you be bossing the job while I go east and get O'Brien out of jail? Mooney and Donahue will see to it that nobody talks back to you."

Placing her hands impulsively on his shoulders, she looked up at him with sparkling eyes. "Oh, I'd just love it. And I don't need protection, although it's kind of you, J.J., to offer it."

McShane removed her hands gently while he muttered, "A young woman, and pretty at that, bossing a big work force of wild Irish. It can't be done."

Pippa caught his arm. "There's room for only two more on the *Shamrock*. Come, and when we get there, I'll show you that it can be done."

＊　　＊　　＊　　＊

When the *Shamrock* reached Hartwell's Basin every farmer driving a dirt-loaded wagon was swearing at his horses. Those farmers who were shoveling sand and gravel into their wagons were cursing the intruding Irish. The high-pitched voices of the Irish responded as they kicked the farmers from the wagon seats and ordered them to do something they understood, like digging and loading. McShane, surveying the scene, said to Pippa,

"Sure now, Colleen, there seems to be some misunderstanding over there. Could you straighten out the matter?"

Pippa flashed a blaze of appreciation. "Just watch me."

Pippa ran to the nearest wagon, where a brawny farmer was trying to unseat an Irishman who had dispossessed him and acquired the reins. Coming up behind the farmer, she lifted his hat, tapped him on the head with the butt of a heavy knife, replaced the hat, caught him as he staggered, and with the aid of the Irish driver heaved him up on the mound of sand in the wagon. Springing up beside him she waved her arms and shouted, "Silence."

As the bickering subsided she shouted, turning slightly so that all could hear,

"Farmers attend!—stop yawping and listen, you backwoods mistakes! There has never been any reason for you to hurry except when a mother bear or a swarm of bees was chasing you. Your horses are by nature industrious, but they've acquired the habit of laziness from you. The Irish do two minutes work in one and try to squeeze in part of a third. So from now on the Irish will drive. Only they can teach the horses how to move all over when they do move. Farmers will help the rest of the Irish to shovel sand and gravel on and off the wagons. We work from sunrise to sunset with a half-hour rest at noon. Any farmer who lags will receive a slap from a shovel on the seat of his pants. Irishmen demonstrate!"

Resounding whacks sparked corresponding bellows of laughter. Pippa jumped down and ran to McShane, her face upturned for approval. Unsmiling, McShane spoke rapidly,

"Across the brook there must be built a stone-block arch one-hundred-and-fifty-feet long, twenty-five-feet high and wide enough to span the brook. Have the men rig a pile driver on each side of the brook and sink twenty-foot logs straight down into the quicksand and keep driving them one on top of the other until they strike hard pan under the quicksand. Then lay solid mats of twelve-inch timbers on the piles and another mat crisscross if necessary. They will be bases for the legs of the arch.

"Be driving the piles at once because the arch must be built before they can proceed to the middle with the embankment. Persuade farmers from Pittsford clear up to Rochester to bring teams and wagons, or wheelbarrows if they have no horses, and dump sand or gravel on the west side, building toward the center."

In a disappointed tone Pippa asked, "What do you suggest as a method for persuading farmers?"

McShane's steel-blue eyes twinkled as he took some shillings from his pocket and pressed them into her hand.

"While persuading a farmer, pass these from one hand to the other. Make them jingle. Accidentally drop one. Search, but fail to find it. After you've gone he'll find it and come running after you to return it."

"He will like—."

McShane interrupted, "Sure now, do it your own way. In the end you always get it. Farewell, Colleen, Mavourneen. I'll be poling down the canal in a small boat to the Schoharie, taking two men to spell me with the poles. After I've released O'Brien I'll pole on to Alexander's Mills below Schenectady. Superintendent Wright and Engineer White have asked me to meet them there. They must decide on how to build a canal channel through a five-mile gorge made by the Mohawk River before it falls into the Hudson."

       ❖   ❖   ❖   ❖

Pippa's eyes were clouded with resentment as she watched McShane, poling a bateau, disappear around a northward bend in the canal. Instead of a word of praise he had just given her more instructions. When she turned back to the turmoil of Irishmen and farmers her heart sank. All work had stopped. Mooney came to her casting angry looks over his shoulder. Touching a forefinger to a lock on his sweaty brow he said,

"The farmers have struck. They claim that Mr. Nathan Roberts has built a navigable channel from the east bank of the Genesee River opposite Rochester to the other side of this valley where we're building the west end of this embankment. He's now digging a channel west of Rochester toward what they call the Mountain Ridge near Lake Ontario. The farmers have a road from Hartwell's Basin along that narrow swamp on the south side of this embankment, across the valley and up the other side to the canal head where homemade boats are waiting to carry freight from the east to the Genesee, where there's a road across the almost-dry river bed to Rochester."

Pippa snorted, "I haven't seen any freight boats coming here from the east."

"Look behind you, Miss. One coming around the far bend."

Pippa looked and became thoughtful. "Give the assembly whistle of the Tipperary Ten and follow me to the *Shamrock*. Be quick."

Unloading of the *Shamrock* was stopped, and the horses were hitched to the rope at the eastern end. With Pippa and the Ten aboard, it started back. A mile down the canal it was steered so as to force the oncoming freight boat against the tow path. Including the driver and the captain, the freight boat had a crew of five. They were no match for the Ten. Pippa daubed the dirty faces of the crew with white flour stirred in grease. Then from a small box of rouge she dotted their faces, necks, and the backs of their hands—as well as the captain's bald head—with spots of red. Speaking sternly she gave them an order,

"Don't rub off any of that. If they ask you, just tell people that you have small pox. After unloading your freight at the head, don't wait for a return load. Just go back."

Pippa returned to the *Shamrock*. The Ten concealed themselves in the freighter and in low, fierce tones directed the crew.

At the head of navigation, farmers in their wagons crowded noisily. Under the stern eyes of the Ten the spectral-looking crew silently unloaded the freight boat. Watching the crew the farmers also became silent, fascinated. After a while they looked at each other. Finally a voice asked, "What ails them?"

Another voice replied, "Looks like small pox, and bad!"

Came a scraping of wheels as a wagon was turned around and a third voice proclaimed, "Anyone touches them barrels, bales, and boxes is liable to catch small pox. I'm going back to haulin' sand. What d'ye say, Jake?"

Discussing the possibility of an epidemic, the other farmers turned their wagons into line and drove back to the sand and gravel pits.

When the unloaded freight boat returned to the idly-floating *Shamrock*, Pippa took five of the Ten aboard the *Shamrock*, dotted the other five with red spots, and ordered them to accompany the freight boat eastward to its home port. They were to permit no one to say that they had small pox, but were to show themselves whenever the boat passed a lock and let people draw conclusions. If asked where they had been they could reply, "Rochester."

Nearing the home port of the freighter, the five were to frighten the crew into desertion, to man the boat themselves, and to continue wearing the red spots until a number of people along the canal had seen them. Then they might desert at the home port and pole in a rented bateau back to Hartwell's Basin.

After the freighter had gone Pippa appropriated one of the wagons, had the five load it with part of the freight, and drove it to Rochester where she delivered it. She continued during the next four days, delivering all of it. A few more freighters arrived. She delivered their cargoes. Then boats stopped coming. Pippa returned to the sand pit and resumed driving a wagon. That way she could keep better track of what was going on. In her heart burned a desire that McShane would somehow hear of and appreciate her skill in coping with critical incidents. Daily she watched for his return.

After more than nine hundred piles had been driven into the banks where the canal line crossed Irondequoit Creek, the stone arch was built with blocks cut from a nearby ledge and joined with cement brought in by the *Shamrock*. But not until the embankment had been built all the way across did McShane return, bringing O'Brien.

Instead of being overjoyed Pippa was emotionally relieved. She greeted McShane casually from the seat of a wagon load of sand. Nor did she converse with him until he had sought her out the next day. In a cordial tone such as he would have used for any of the Ten he tilted his Irish hat and said,

"Sure, Colleen, 'Tis a fine piece of work, but the sand and gravel will neither hold water nor keep the prism shape of a channel. Would you be knowing if there's a bed of blue clay hereabouts? A farmer showed me some last summer, but I can't remember where it was."

"One of the farmers told me that we'd never get water across that embankment unless we puddled the channel with blue clay. That means lining the channel with a three-inch inner coating of clay and letting the sun harden it."

"Sure now I know what puddling means. But where's the clay to be found?"

"He'll tell you. His name is Nathan Roberts."

"Nathan Roberts? He's no farmer. He was a school-master, and now a canal engineer. Where do you see him?"

Pippa jumped down from the wagon. "Over there with another farmer whose ears stick up through his hat."

Without a word McShane deserted Pippa and strode toward Roberts. Pippa's erect figure lost some of its natural grace. Resolution departed from the firm set of her chin. Her dancing eyes were still as she stared at McShane's broad back. She listened to their exchange of greetings and McShane's recital of what he had seen at the Schoharie and eastward in the gorge. McShane was interested in his own adventures, not in her. She had thrown herself at him. She fancied that all of the men in sight were covertly smil-ing and winking at each other. She fled for the *Shamrock*. It had brought McShane the day before, been unloaded, and was now receiving eastbound passengers. They were coming across the embankment carrying their baggage. In her ears McShane's words were ringing.

"Sure, Nathan, the Littlejohn Schoharie dam held against the spring freshet. The ice went over it like snakes across the back of a sleeping hog. He constructed the dam exactly the way I told him.

"The dam was built to form a pond, into which a lock on the west side drops the boats eight feet below the channel level. There's a big wagon wheel, with raised flanges, lying almost flat on the ground, which turns on a vertical shaft. An inch-and-a-half endless rope goes around the wheel, across the pond, and round a similar wheel on the other side. A sleepy old horse on the west side turns the wheel when a boat is crossing either way. The boat takes its horses aboard on a gangplank and is tied to the rope going in the direction the captain wants the boat to cross. It's released and poled through the lock if on the east side, because it's gates are nearly always standing open since it acts as a feeder for the eastward channel as far as Schenectady. Beyond that lock the captain drops the gangplank to the tow path and discharges and hitches his horses.

"Boats going west are steadied by a fixed rope stretched across a little below the revolving rope."

While talking, McShane had been standing with his back to the *Shamrock*. As it started moving Roberts interrupted him,

"A young woman on that boat seems to be trying to attract your attention. She's waving good-bye."

Without turning his head McShane replied, "The colleen has a wild streak. She likes to be in the wilderness with canal gangs. After a few months of it, she becomes angry with someone, usually me, and returns to her home in Utica. She has her cap set for Talcott. After a while she's in a

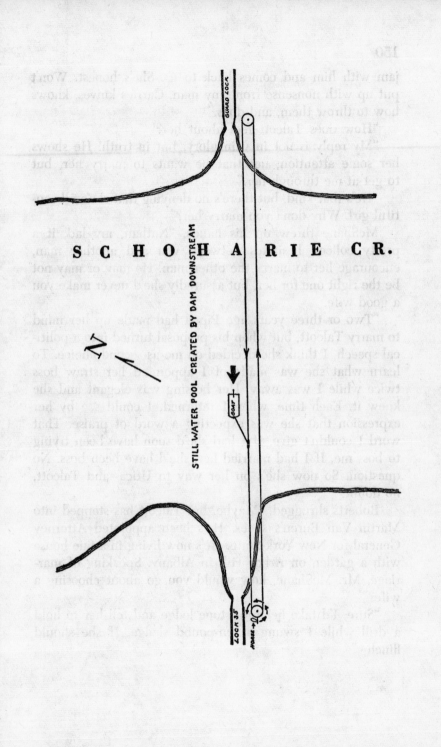

jam with him and comes back to us. She's honest. Won't put up with nonsense from any man. Carries knives, knows how to throw them, and does."

"How does Talcott feel about her?"

"My reply is not in vain glory, but in truth. He shows her some attention; not that he wants to marry her, but to get at me through her."

"He's that kind, but there's no denying that she's a beautiful girl. Why don't you marry her?"

McShane threw up his hands. "Nathan, my lad, if a pretty colleen hesitates between you and another man, encourage her to marry the other man. He may or may not be the right one for her, but assuredly she'd never make you a good wife.

"Two or three years ago Pippa had made up her mind to marry Talcott, but when his proposal turned into a political speech, I think she decided on me as second choice. To learn what she was made of I appointed her straw boss twice while I was away. Her bossing was elegant and she knew it. Each time, when I returned, I could see by her expression that she was expecting a word of praise. That word I couldn't give. If I had she'd soon have been trying to boss me. If I had married her, she'd have been boss. No question. So now she's on her way to Utica—and Talcott, no doubt."

Roberts shrugged, "Maybe, but Talcott has stepped into Martin Van Buren's shoes. He's been appointed Attorney General for New York State. He's now living in a fine house with a garden on Arbor Hill in Albany. Speaking of marriage, Mr. McShane, how would you go about choosing a wife?"

"Sure, I'd take her to a stone ledge and tell her to hold a drill while I swung a ten-pound sledge. If she should flinch—"

"You'd hit her on the head with the sledge?"

"Nathan, you're being facetious."

"Maybe. Tell me, Mr. McShane, how are the engineers planning to run the canal around the river gorge below Schenectady."

"Sure now, they're not. During summer while the river is low they observe that from Alexander's Mills on the south bank there's a dry stretch of round stones and gravel interspersed with small puddles two-thirds of the way across to the north bank. Alexander's Mills is the beginning of the gorge, where there is no bank but high cliffs on the north side of the river and low cliffs on the south. Since the canal must have water and there is no water of consequence in the hills between Schenectady and Albany, especially in the summer, the canal must be in the bed of the river— and no help for it. At Alexander's Mills the river bends to the northeast. The set of the current being in the same direction, the river has washed a deep groove along the base of the precipice. By digging the groove wider and dumping the gravel and stones in a long bank which will run parallel with the precipice and about seventy-five feet out, and maybe to shovel up some gravel from the river bed on the other side of the bank, it can be built higher than flood water. Of course they'll be mixing branches and brush with the gravel as they build, and they'll reinforce it with logs at the base.

"The top will be a ten-foot-wide tow path with a guard rail. The channel will cross the river at Alexander's Mills on an all-stone aqueduct and lock down to the canal in the river. A guard lock will admit water to the channel from the river as needed.

"Eight miles down-river the channel will cross back to the south bank on another stone aqueduct. Sixteen locks will take the canal down through Cohoes. It will enter Hudson River at Watervliet. Passenger boats will continue in the canal channel to Erie Basin at the foot of State Street in Albany."

"And how many years will be required to finish all of that?"

"Sure they'll finish that end of the canal by autumn of next year."

"When do we finish at this end?"

McShane's assured manner vanished, his expression became thoughtful. After a long silence he said slowly, "Now, I don't know. I've examined that Mountain Ridge, the Great Barrier. I sometimes wonder if we'll ever finish this end. If we do, 'twill be on our hands and knees."

Chapter 8

TAKING ADVANTAGE OF McShane's mood Roberts persuaded him to cut a channel across the embankment at once and puddle it with blue clay. Roberts' point was that the embankment would continue to settle and gully from rain for many years. He had built a feeder dam across the Genesee River which supplied the canal with water through a ditch where it came close to the river bank, after skirting Cobb Hill, a quarter mile up-river from the proposed site of the Rochester aqueduct. He wanted McShane to see it. As soon as his men were well started in cutting a prism across the embankment and holding it in place with blue clay which the farmers brought in their wagons, McShane condescended to go.

McShane was astonished at the practical construction of the quarter-mile-long feeder ditch edging the east bank of the Genesee and the durable dam only one timber high. The dam was merely two courses of eighteen-inch squared-timbers, parallel and four feet apart, laid by means of chiseling a flat surface in the bedrock of the river. Each timber had been bored every five feet, and holes had been drilled in the bedrock to match those in the timbers. Depressions in the bedrock had been filled with cement so that water wouldn't pass beneath the timbers. Threaded bolts set in the holes with cement and passed through the timbers anchored them to the river bottom. Stones and gravel filled the four-foot space between timbers. Roberts explained,

"This feeder dam could be built only when the river was at summer low. Right now the dam is forcing enough water into the ditch to fill the canal to a depth of two feet from the east bank to Pittsford. Fall rains will raise it to a four-foot depth. When you finish your channel across the embankment, we can easily join the two ends and have navigation from the Genesee at Rochester to Little Falls. Governor Clinton's term expires the First of January. This might help him when he seeks reelection."

"If he does? A Tipperary Irishman would prefer making a career of conferring with canal engineers and guiding the building of the canal to the governor's job of settling political quarrels."

Roberts raised an eyebrow, but when he spoke it was about building the aqueduct.

"William Britton, after building the wall around Auburn Prison, brought convict labor here a year ago to build the aqueduct. He lodged them on the island between the Rochester and Fitzhugh Race. He paid no wages, but the convicts wouldn't work much except when trying to escape. Britton cut blocks from a limestone ledge on the west bank. He bolted the foundation blocks of his piers to the river bed and seated them with cement. Last spring, after the freshet, only the bolts remained. They were bent downstream and nearly flat. So limestone won't do.

"I've found gray sandstone near Carthage, but I don't trust it for piers in the Genesee. My only hope is Onondaga limestone, which contains a percentage of flint."

"Now where did you find it?"

"In the Walton Tract a little to the south of White Lake and southeast of Cossitts. It's six miles by road from the canal."

"Have you considered the cost of dragging blocks four-feet square on a stone boat by oxen down from those steep hills? Decending a grade, slippery with mud, an overloaded stone boat could get out of hand and you'd have no way of stopping it. Your oxen would be killed. I know those hills.

"Nathan lad, take your men to the Genesee crossing and chisel beds for pier foundations six-inches deep. If, due to natural depressions the beds are uneven, level them with cement. How many arches?"

"Nine of fifty-foot-span and a small arch at each end. Width of arch up and downstream will be forty feet."

"Provide cement and iron clamps to cramp the base blocks together, and plenty of long, two-inch threaded bolts, sledges, and drills."

"But the stone, Mr. McShane?"

"Nathan, from the township of Greece I'll deliver by boat, from a short lateral canal connecting with the Erie Canal, blocks of red sandstone cut to size. I'll dig six feet to reach the stone, and I'll deliver it at a wooden chute on the Rochester bank of the Genesee. The blocks will slide down to you faster than you can lay them. When it's too cold to float blocks to you, I'll slide 'em over the ice on sleds. To prevent wet cement from freezing during the winter mix it with salt. I predict that by this time next year loaded boats will float across the new aqueduct. Now I'll be taking my choir to the sandstone quarry to be."

"Your choir?"

"Sure now, haven't you heard Irishmen sing to the clinking of hammers and chisels on stone? Take off a couple of hours some noon and visit our quarry. You'll hear some sweet music."

• • • •

Farmers with teams and wagons worked from dawn until dusk. The Irish worked the same hours, and for a few more hours by bonfire and torchlight, digging a prism-shaped channel across the Irondequoit embankment and puddling it with blue clay. McShane allowed seven days for the clay to harden, then introduced a foot of water from the channel which Roberts had meanwhile extended from

Pittsford to the embankment. After two days of watching he raised the water level another foot. Still the blue clay retained without leaking. Not daring to increase the pressure until the following spring, McShane declared the embankment open to navigation for boats with a draft of not more than twenty inches.

He sent the *Shamrock* eastward to proclaim that the small pox epidemic at Rochester had run its course and ended. When the Pittsford farmers complained because there was no more work, McShane reminded them that if they would work longer hours than ever they might get their fall plowing done before freeze-up.

McShane led his men to Greece township, built a winter camp, and dug six feet of earth from the red sandstone shelf one hundred yards long and twenty wide. He roofed a portion with logs, poles, and brush. Protected from the wind as the weather became colder, his men opened a red sandstone quarry.

Roberts, who had studied mineralogy, analyzed the stone as a mixture of quartz sand, magnesium, calcium carbonate, and red oxide of iron, with a silica binder. As it was extracted it was comparatively soft and quite easily worked. After a few days of exposure it became very hard.

Roberts ventured that red sandstone properly seated and cemented could withstand indefinitely the full force of the Genesee under any and all conditions. He walked through snow from the Genesee to the quarry to praise McShane for his discovery. Speaking gruffly, McShane told him that if there were any complaints he'd listen, but he didn't have time to lend an ear to praise. Therefore Roberts had better return and go to work. Abashed and hurt, Roberts walked back shaking his head.

With the luck of the Irish McShane had opened his quarry close to the edge of the red sandstone ledge. By drilling rows of holes, filling each with powder and a fuse, and tamping the powder down with clay, he blasted loose long blocks two-feet wide and eighteen-inches deep. At the edge of the quarry he built a fulcrum of short pieces of squared timbers with a hole bored in the center. A peeled forty-foot hickory log, bored two-thirds from the butt, was joined loosely to the fulcrum by a long bolt. To the tip end of the log a block of sandstone was attached by a double hitch. The butt end was then pulled down by a short rope. On the principle of a well lift, the stone block was raised above the ground, swung in a half circle, and lowered gently on a flat boat in the lateral canal.

The third time the flat boat returned Roberts was aboard. To McShane he spoke anxiously,

"Can you cut that stone a little faster? I can't keep my men busy. The late fall rains are almost due. If we haven't built the bases in the bedrock of the river for nine fifty-foot-arches and two smaller end arches before the water rises we can't start until the dry season next summer."

McShane shook his head. "It's the blasting powder, Nathan. I'm buying the best to be had in Rochester. It's fine for blasting a squirrel off a limb, but pitifully weak for opening seams in bedrock red sandstone. At that, the stores will sell me only half of what I ask for. When are the Oneida County Welsh coming?"

"Tomorrow on the *Shamrock*, I'll send them right over with a half of my men. But what good will that do since you can't get enough powder?"

"Sure I've found some seams and fissures. With enough men we can feather-wedge out a lot of it. Also we can heat the rock by building fires on it after drilling, and then pour water on it. Boys can do that. I've sent O'Brien into Rochester to catch some."

Roberts smiled and looked at the sky. "Doesn't look like rain now. Pray that it holds off. Any of your men know how to cut timbers for arch forms and build 'em?"

"Sure, I'll be sending you thirty tomorrow."

"Send 'em westward along the canal. They'll find some oak. Tell 'em to cut it, quarter it, and raft it. When ready I'll send a yoke of oxen to drag the rafts to the Genesee. Don't know how all these plans will turn out. One thing to say it; and another to do it."

McShane laid a hand on Robert's shoulder. "I'm truly sorry for you, Nathan, because you have no Irish blood. As you are, you look at the dark side of things and become fainthearted. If you were Irish, you'd go after that dark side as if you couldn't wait to get to it—like a prize fighter going after his opponent. The Irish may die fighting, but they never fail."

Roberts studied McShane's eyes. "I have none of the qualifications, it's true. But I can try to be like an Irishman."

McShane slapped him on the shoulder. "Sure! And if you stick to it, you might convince us that you do have a drop of Irish in you from way back. If you would be Irish, remember, don't stop to catch your breath until you're coughing up blood."

* * * * *

Next day, when Jones ap Kerig and his Oneida County Welsh arrived, McShane greeted him wearily but in a kindly tone,

"Last time we met, and I think it was also the first, I knocked you spinning on your backside with one wallop. When they carried you away, Jonesey, you were laughing and crying and arguing with yourself about which could be the butt end of a goat."

"You took advantage of me, McShane. At the moment you hit me my right hand was extended to you in warm friendship. I'd like another go at you."

"Your left hand holding a rock was hidden behind you. That rock being under when you fell was the pivot on which you spun. But our games must come later. Casey will show you the oak trees. Have them down and quartered. The form for the arches must be abuilding by tomorrow night. The sky is overcast. We've only hours left before the rain."

As Casey guided the Welsh westward, the flat boat arrived empty. McShane ordered the crew to follow the Welsh and bring back as many branches, bark pieces, and scraps as they could, and to return for more. An oak-chip fire would heat rock. He wanted as many fires as possible.

Daily the sky became more threatening, the air more chilly, but no rain fell. Cutting great slots in the limestone river bed, filling depressions with grouting, and leveling until the bubble in a spirit level stood at center everywhere in the bottom of each slot took time. Placing precisely-faced sandstone blocks on the still-wet cement of the bottoms of the slots so that the upright iron bolts set in the slots came up through the holes drilled in the blocks as smoothly as a knife in a sheath, and cramping the blocks together with iron clamps took even more time. And the plan required ten slots, including the two end arches.

In every man's heart rang and echoed the word, "impossible." The time was too short. The air was blue with autumn haze. Masses of fog rolled in from Lake Ontario. Roberts and ap Kerig's men had snatched food while they worked. They hadn't slept for nights. Exhausted, disheartened, and famished they were ready to give up. The Irish were in a holy glow. The sharper the challenge the greater their determination and the harder they worked. Their eyes were dark with fatigue, their faces grim; *they were the silent people*. At two hour intervals all day and night, stone blocks and oak timbers, bored and supplied with dowels, roared down the chute to the river bed. Bonfires and torches provided illumination. Rochester people said later that the river bottom had looked like Inferno with all the lost souls toiling away.

Incredibly, though slowly, the gigantic bases of the arches began to rise. A foot—two feet—and then a little faster. Four more days and nights would be required to build the bases and brace the forms so that they too could withstand high water. But the masonry must rise at the same pace to support them.

The third night it rained, gently at first, then rather hard. Toward morning it stopped. The current of the Genesee had increased. The bedrock was rendered wet and slippery. The casks of cement had had to be covered with tarpaulins. The morning brought fair weather, and with it came the Irish swarming down the banks, joining Roberts' men and the Welsh without disturbing or upsetting them. Enough timbers and stone blocks had been supplied for the final effort.

Exhausted men, bone weary, stumbled against each other and dropped tools and materials. The sun, having been hidden for days, was reassuring to all but McShane. His voice rasped an alarm note,

"At sundown expect heavy rain beginning with thunder showers. The stone work must go up eighteen-inches higher to be safe. This is the last dash. This is it! Welshmen! Have you the guts to do it?"

Inspired by the example of the Irish, they showed they had. Hours later when the setting sun sank into slaty clouds boiling up from the south and southwest and lightning flashes duelled along the horizon, McShane called,

"Enough! We've done it. Find your tools, kegs of cement, your jackets, everything. There may have been a cloudburst south of us. There may be a flood. Get up that west bank as fast as you can."

In the chill darkness the Genesee rose angrily and muddily, foaming and swirling, but it did not flood. The storm swung counterclockwise northward. The laborers had taken cover in the barns in which they had been sleeping. From houses near the west bank of the river, people peering through rain-lashed windows saw a gaunt, bareheaded man walking at the edge of the bank. He lingered long enough to see the squat stone piers toss up plumes of foam. At last with a gesture of contempt McShane turned toward the sandstone quarry and found a leaky hut into which he crawled and fell asleep.

That storm ended summer and ushered in winter, but the river current receded enough so that temporary foot-bridges could enable the construction to continue. Three weeks later the thermometer dropped to zero overnight. McShane had prepared for it at the quarry by drilling rows of holes eight-inches deep in the sandstone, near the edge of the ledge, one foot between holes and two feet between rows. All the holes had been filled with water.

During the night McShane was kept joyously awake by pops and snaps as the freezing water expanded and opened long fissures in the rock. Feather-wedging would easily open them deeper and wider. Later in the morning when Roberts came and saw what McShane had accomplished, he shook his head and spoke with admiration,

"None, but the McShane."

McShane changed the topic. "Nathan, who has charge of blasting out lock chambers at the first rise of the Mountain Ridge?"

"Jonathan Child is trying to open a channel in the dolomite two-thirds of the way up, while David Bates farther down the rock slope is opening five double lock chambers. David Thomas is in a swamp somewhere southeast of them cutting a mile-long ditch which will divert the south fork of Tonawanda Creek into Oak Orchard Creek. And that's necessary. Oak Orchard is the only considerable flow crossing the canal between Mountain Ridge and Brockport."

"How are Child and Bates doing?"

"Poorly. They are blasting in seepage from the swamps on the top of the ridge. The whole face of that rock slope is wet all of the time excepting in winter, when it's icy. Powder gets damp when poured in holes in that rock, and it loses much of its feeble power. Why do you ask?"

"Because I'm leading my men, draft animals, and wagons loaded with tools and blankets westward on the Seneca Turnpike tomorrow, leaving you in charge here. It's becoming too tame to suit me."

"Or perhaps you're thinking about the Mountain Ridge and the men who are working there. Something in your heart keeps whispering that they may be unable to cut a fifty-foot-wide channel through that nine miles of dolomite rock which rises a hundred feet above the eastern plain. They may have encountered unforeseen obstacles which they can't overcome. And thus you build in your mind a scene of disaster. The McShane to the rescue!"

McShane gave Roberts a quick glance. "You wouldn't be poking fun at me, Nathan?"

Roberts flushed, "Indeed no, J.J. I may have sounded like it, but I meant it seriously. I can finish building this aqueduct, but only you can lick the Mountain Ridge. The sooner you go the better."

McShane laid a hand on Roberts' shoulder. "By spring you'll have enough stone cut so that the Oneida County Welsh can finish the aqueduct. Take your men to Brockport and resume work on the channel. You must build embankments across three ravines all deeper than Irondequoit. Owing to the lack of feeder streams along the route, you won't be filling the channel behind you; so there'll be no *Shamrock* following with supplies until you reach Oak Orchard Creek. There you'll be close to Mountain

Ridge. As for me, my supplies must come from Buffalo through Tonawanda Village and thence over a pair of ruts twenty miles to the Mountain Ridge. During winter the ruts are often so covered that you don't know where you are. So the Irish must go in with sledges, drills, picks, shovels, and little else to lick the Mountain Ridge. Belike it has already licked Jonathan Child and David Bates."

Roberts gripped McShane's hard hand. "J.J., I'll try to break through to the Mountain Ridge by next September so that you can get your supplies from the *Shamrock*."

McShane shook his head. "You'll do well to make it by a year from September. Cut off from all support, the Irish will lick that Ridge with bare hands."

Three days later Roberts accompanied the Irish to the Seneca Turnpike and watched them walk leaning into a blinding snowstorm from the west. Their hunched shoulders and fluttering rags reminded him of his grandfather's description of Washington and his troops at Valley Forge drilling during a storm.

Chapter 9

SLEEPING NIGHTS in hastily-constructed brush shelters, where frequently-replenished campfires helped to keep them from freezing, the Irish succeeded in reaching Buffalo eight days later. McShane lodged them in barns and arranged for their meals in various houses. They were served between family mealtimes, and although certain housewives endured long hours in their kitchens, they were paid for it.

Alone McShane tramped through deep snow to Niagara Falls to confer with General Peter B. Porter,* Canal Commissioner and public-spirited man. McShane introduced himself and stated briefly that he was leading two-hundred Irishmen in a winter assault on Mountain Ridge. He said that their boots and clothing were too worn to protect them from winter's cold, and before starting north into the snowy wilderness they must have new greased-leather boots, woolen socks, gloves, overjackets, fur-lined caps, as well as leather and woolen repair materials. Furthermore, sleighs loaded with food supplies must come in every week.

Astonished, Porter asked, "What can you accomplish in there during winter? Bates and Child and their men have been working in there all summer and fall. Now they're coming out and won't return until spring."

McShane nodded grimly. "If we should meet 'em, we'll turn 'em back. Sure, winter is the best time for breaking rock."

---

* Porter had been Secretary of State for New York. He was twice elected to Congress, served with distinction in the War of 1812, and surveyed the boundary between United States and Canada west to Wisconsin.

Porter's moon face became incredulous. "Why, man, don't you know that snow gets into holes drilled in rock and wets your blasting powder?"

"I do. We won't be using powder."

"Then how—" (a glint in McShane's eye made him pause and alter his sentence) "will you remove masses of broken rock from your excavation?"

"Sure, I was about to ask for a dozen bull wheels. Never heard of them? A bull wheel has four iron spokes, in the center a mounded iron pivot which will fit snugly in an inverted iron cup let into the base of a foot-square timber thirty or forty feet high. That timber is called the mast. At the bottom it is securely braced by a low crib of short lengths of logs. The rim of the wheel is channel iron. A rope in the channel rotates the mast in a half-turn one way. Reversing the rope turns it back. In England they call the contraption a derrick."

McShane then explained his plan of drilling rows of holes in the rock and filling them with water day and night during the winter so that the natural expansion of freezing water would break loose huge quantities of rock. Large fragments could be further broken by fire and water.

General Porter banged the table and demanded that fire and water be used concomitantly with the drilling. When McShane asked the general if *he* hadn't caught fire, he replied with another bang that he certainly had. Until that moment he had despaired of ever cutting a channel across the Mountain Ridge. Now he was certain that it could be done. The method of freezing water to split rock had been suggested and presumably tried, but it had been reported impracticable. Now he understood why. Not wishing to spend a winter in such a bleak, windy spot, the contractors had used the alleged failure of ice to split rock as an excuse for returning to Buffalo for the winter.

General Porter said that storms sweeping across the

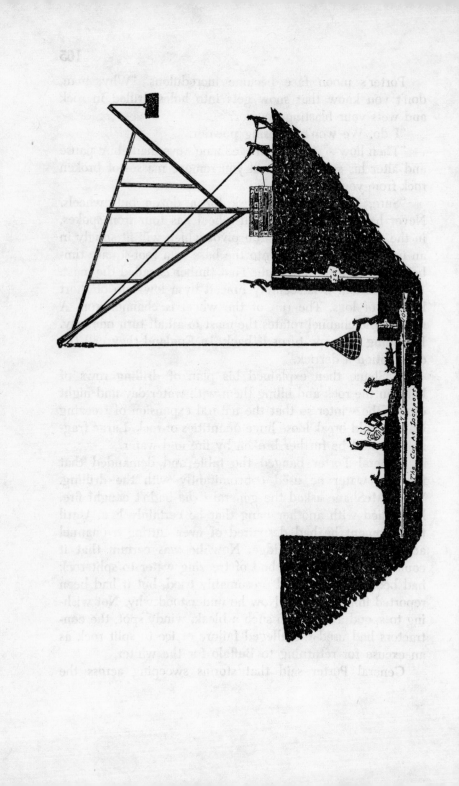

Great Lakes dropped the moisture they had gathered as rain or snow when they struck Mountain Ridge, and the whole area was wet—soaked with water creeping over the rock beneath the covering of root-entangled forest mould. However he knew of one dry spot on the brow near the excavations for locks, about a mile-and-a-half east of the ridge crest. Immediately he would send carpenters and woodchoppers out there to build two log bunk houses and a cook shack. In the meanwhile he would have to ferry wagons across the Niagara River to Canada since Fort Erie was the only trading post where the quality and quantity of boots and clothing which McShane required could be bought. For the present he'd see that the resting Irish had plenty of beef, potatoes, cabbage, and whiskey. He'd also get the blacksmiths to work on the metal parts for the derricks they'd need to raise the broken rock out of the channel and the locks.

Three weeks later two-hundred Irishmen, a few Welsh, and a scattering of mixed origin and uncertain antecedents followed a long train of supply sleighs through ankle-deep snow. Leaving Tonawanda Village at clear sunrise they walked through a cathedral of snow-crested giant hemlocks singing. Toward noon General Porter, having ridden ahead to break trail, called back that David Bates and Jonathan Child and their men, supposedly engaged in blasting out the five double lock chambers in the eastern brow of Mountain Ridge, were coming down the trail, apparently quitting. Porter asked McShane to force them to return to their work.

At McShane's command Irish spread out and caught them as they were scattering. When Porter confronted Bates and Child, their excuse was that they had heard from the carpenters building the new bunk houses that the Irish were coming, and they didn't like Irishmen.

Porter snorted, "You started for home too late. Now you'll have to learn to like them."

The partly-finished bunk houses sheltered everyone, although not warmly. Next morning McShane and Porter surveyed two partially-opened lock chambers at the bottom of the sloping rock. Porter asked deferentially what McShane thought of it.

McShane shook his head. "They should have started cutting at the top. Then, all the broken pieces of stone which they threw out would have rolled to the bottom in a big heap. Sure when they had finished cutting all but the bottom pair of locks that heap would be in the way, but four kegs of powder properly placed and ignited at one time would remove it. The way they're going at it, each pair of lock chambers will be filled by fragments from cutting the next pair of locks above. Time and labor will be lost cleaning out each chamber.

Porter stirred uneasily. "Time is very important. What can you suggest?"

"Bring your carpenters down here. Roof that cutting with planks bored at each end. We'll drill holes in the rock and bolt down the planks. They'll protect the work that has been done."

"Sorry, McShane, but if I take the carpenters from their work they won't finish the bunk house roofs, and you'll sleep cold again tonight."

"Cold we shall be, but not sleeping. We'll be working by bonfire light."

"Get your men started, McShane. You'll find the limits of each lock marked by iron pins driven in the rock. You know the depth of cutting to be made. Afterward I'll explain the reason for haste."

By nightfall McShane had detailed a few gangs to the removal of snow and earthy mould which covered the rock. Other gangs cut wood, built fires on the canal line—up the slope, over the brow, and on beyond toward the crest—and kept them going. More gangs melted snow in kettles over the fires and poured the water in the holes which the sledge and drill men had prepared. Specialists sought cracks and seams in the face of the sloping rock into which they could poke thawed earth and mould to form a bottom five inches down, or deeper if possible. Every yard or so in the cracks they built a plug up to the surface, and in the pockets thus formed they poured water. Impressed with the hustle and bustle, Porter passed among the groups with pails of sweetened hot tea and earthenware mugs strung by their handles on a stick. Toward midnight McShane came to him and said that he could listen for a few minutes, but the whole operation was in such a critical state that there wasn't time to sit down.

Porter picked him up with this statement: "The United States is in an even more critical condition. In the year eighteen-hundred-and-nineteen, due in part to the unwise demand of the United States Bank in Philadelphia that all state banks redeem their notes with specie, state banks began to fail. They are still failing, and thousands of enterprises and private fortunes are ruined. Our national economy is in a crisis. In that same year John Quincy Adams insisted that our draft of the Florida Treaty with Spain bear a clause which would recognize Texas as having been a part of the Louisiana Territory since eighteen-hundred-and-three. But William Crawford, favored as a presidential nominee by Georgia, Virginia, and the Albany Regency, persuaded President Monroe to strike out that clause to prevent Adams from gaining prestige. The best interests of the United States were sacrificed to promote the ambition of one rather insignificant man. That's American politics, but probably it's no worse than politics in other countries."

Keeping an anxious eye on his gangs, McShane nodded. Porter continued, "Hitherto, presidential electors have been chosen by the legislature. That system gives the Regency control, and naturally they are opposed to change. DeWitt Clinton, John Quincy Adams, Colden, and Andrew Jackson favor choosing electors by popular vote. Clinton tried unsuccessfully to have such a bill passed while he was governor, and he's still pushing it. The People's Party has come out for it, and they like Clinton. However, to win their backing Clinton needs some notable success such as your breaking a channel through this Mountain Ridge."

"How soon?"

"By the end of next winter."

"And if we don't?"

"Then the United States may not be united much longer. Two forces bind a country together: foreign conquest and commerce. Many forces are tearing us apart. Our foreign wars seem ended; our commerce is only sectional. We must have better communication and transportation—canals everywhere so that we can do business with each other more easily. Immediately there will be a new spirit in the country, and we'll begin to feel like one country. But it must come soon, McShane, very soon."

"Then it's up to the Irish?"

"Well—yes. No other people have the determination and the fortitude. Yes, it's up to the Irish to save the country from itself. Do you understand?"

"Sure now, I do. We have a similar condition in Ireland. Some of the people in Belfast, and indeed pretty much everywhere in Ulster County, prefer doing business with England instead of with the southern counties. 'Tis a stain on the fair name of Ireland. It must not happen here. General, the Irish will do their part. Send us as many kegs of Canadian gunpowder as you can when there's no snow on the ground. We think the Massachusetts powder from Ives and Loomis, and Laflin and Loomis is adulterated with powdered charcoal by Regency hirelings as it comes through Albany. It's not strong enough to break up solid ledge like this.

"Thin clothes for summer and food the year around."

"Agreed, McShane."

*　　*　　*　　*

During the winter of 1823, McShane by forcing his men to the limit of strength and endurance, and by toiling seven days a week regardless of the weather, carved with precision five pairs of lock chambers, each connecting with the one above it. Each had a twelve-foot lift and a three-foot depth for water. When filled, the highest lock would have a water level that matched the water in the channel which would be resumed at the brow and extend due west through solid rock to the crest.

At the brow McShane cut straight down thirteen feet through rock. As he cut his way to the crest, a distance of a mile-and-a-half on the channel floor, the cutting had to become deeper until at the crest the channel floor was thirty-feet-six-inches below ground surface. From there, bearing southwestward, the depth of cutting through rock gradually diminished to twelve feet over a distance of seven miles by channel floor. At that point the great rock barrier terminated at the west side as abruptly as it had arisen on the east. There still remained five-and-one-quarter miles of cutting through earth, including a few ledges at first, before reaching the navigable part of Tonawanda Creek. From the confluence of the creek with Niagara River a tow path along the bank would lead to Buffalo and Lake Erie. As nearly as possible, the channel floor from the brow on the eastern side of the ridge to Tonawanda Creek would have to be level and four feet lower than Lake Erie's surface.

McShane's forward cutting always took the form of

crude stairs. As he advanced he continued that form. Each cut was fifty-feet wide and went down in wide steps fifteen to twenty feet deep, or until they reached the level of the tow path. For the last five feet down, the cuts were forty-feet wide, the width of the channel. Instead of being flat on bottom, the channel declined from each side toward the center at an angle just sufficient to drain. The center was a gutter cut in the rock wide and deep enough to discharge surface drainage, rain, and the flow from ruptured courses of subterranean streams. Usually the gutter was choked with detritus, but it could be shovelled out when necessary. The trees removed from the canal line on the ridge were converted into planks and posts for tongue and groove piling and for building lock gates, and they were stacked for seasoning.

By May of 1824 McShane had cut a channel through the ridge for five-and-three-quarters miles and had come to the earth cutting.° When the carpenters came again General Porter was with them. After shaking hands with McShane, he said,

"Sir, you have completed your fundamental work on schedule, and the engineers have inspected it. They found your measurements correct, but they pointed out that the walls and floor are unfinished and need smoothing. They also say that there are several stretches of a hundred yards or more on the tow path which incline toward the channel and that they should be made level. Also the lock gates must be built and hung, but these are things you can easily accomplish next winter and spring.

"Nathan Roberts has encountered difficulties at Sandy Creek which have put him behind schedule, and he cannot

---

° Twice General Porter had sent his carpenters out to build new bunk houses for the Irish as they pushed forward, and he had been generous with clothes, boots, food, and whiskey.

possibly dig the channel to the foot of Mountain Ridge
before next September. Furthermore, the contractors who
undertook those two west-end sections failed because they
were unable to cope with the water seepage from nearby
small swamps.

"The engineers have asked me to arrange with you to
continue the earth excavating you have begun."

McShane nodded acquiescence and continued to look
expectantly at Porter. Porter who was six-inches taller than
McShane looked at the ground and said,

"The Irish have done their part, but, as a politician, I
have failed. Last month on the last day of the legislative
session, Assemblyman John Bowman made a motion with
the tacit consent of Tallmadge, leader of The People's Party,
deposing DeWitt Clinton from the Board of Canal Commissioners. After Tallmadge had spoken in favor of it the
act was passed without debate. Shortly afterward it passed
the Senate. Henry Cunningham, assemblyman from Montgomery County, spoke at the closing and favored Clinton
while shaming the whole legislature. No one applauded his
speech. When the people in the streets heard about it they
chased the assemblymen and senators into their hotels and
boarding houses. And those statesmen were happy to lock
themselves in their rooms to escape being tarred and
feathered!

"And there, sir, you have the power of the Regency on
one hand, and the feeling of the people on the other. Unless someone can think of a way to thwart the Regency, it
is likely that all construction on the Erie Canal will terminate this fall. Indeed all of the Canal Commissioners are
expecting it. No one has any hope."

"That's because none of them are Irish." McShane
paused to fill his clay pipe, "Is there any man in the
Regency who could crack it open if he turned his coat?"

"Well, Marcy and Butler could be unmade by Van Buren as fast as he made them. They know it. So they wouldn't turn. Singly or together they couldn't break Van Buren even if they did turn. Talcott might bring Van Buren to heel for a short time, but he couldn't break him. However, Talcott wouldn't turn; he's not that kind."

"Who could break Van Buren?"

"Only DeWitt Clinton. But he's out and has no way to get a fresh start."

"General, they tell me that the voters will elect a new governor in November. You've said that Tallmadge is boss of the People's Party. Will that party back him for governor?"

"Uncertain. Some of them want John Taylor of Saratoga for their nominee."

"Sure now if they're divided, and the right man suggested Clinton, wouldn't they settle for Clinton?"

"It's anybody's guess."

"Who is the Regency candidate?"

"Colonel Young. But the People's Party hates the Regency so, they won't even look at him."

"Then if Talcott should go to Tallmadge and say that he is quitting the Regency because of Colonel Young and that he will be able to swing a lot of Regency voters behind the People's Party candidate if it is Clinton with Tallmadge for lieutenant governor, wouldn't Tallmadge go for it to get John Taylor out of the way?"

General Porter was silent for a long time. At last he said, "If it were anyone except Tallmadge, I'd say 'no.' But since it's Tallmadge, and although it's a long shot, I say 'yes.' Now how do you propose to persuade Talcott to do something that's foreign to his nature?"

"General, before I can answer that question I must give the matter more thought. However, be assured that while my men are shoring up the sides of this earthen cut with planks and piles, anchored by thick poles nailed to logs buried fifteen feet away, I'll be in the rock cut chiseling off the bumps and thinking about persuading Talcott."

That night, McShane wrote his first letter to Pippa. After sealing it, he dispatched it by O'Brien with an order to bring back a signed receipt. The letter began with:

My Dear Pippa,

For years I have hoped to be in a position such that I could ask you to be my wife. I have never spoken of it because I have believed that you have given your heart to a man who now enjoys a station in life far above what I may hope to attain. I am told he lives in a fine house on Arbor Hill in Albany. You have seen where I live.

With the fall of DeWitt Clinton it seems that the canal cause, on the eve of attainment, has been lost. Only by re-electing Clinton governor can it be saved. Only the man you love can bring that about. Only you can persuade him to do it. For the sake of thousands of Irishmen many of whom have given their lives, been crippled, or have worn out their bodies; for the sake of the unblemished friendship that has developed between you and me (I hope it will continue) I am asking you to see him and persuade him as follows. . . .

On an oppressively hot June evening during the period of full moon, Talcott, returning to his home on Arbor Hill in Albany, found a drawing scrawled on his doorstep in charcoal which showed two figures with joined hands. In his hall on a mahogany lamp table lay a letter addressed to him in a rounded feminine hand, unmistakably Pippa's. During his solitary but ample dinner, with ample whiskey, he read her letter. She was coming to see him, soon. Recalling the joined-hands sketch on his doorstep, Talcott asked his butler if she had already called. The reply being negative, he asked if neighboring children had played there. Again the reply was negative. After reflection the butler

PIPPA

volunteered that the gardener had seen a vagrant disappearing among the lawn shrubs during the afternoon and had pursued, but the vagrant had escaped up the hill.

After dinner Talcott spent an hour at his desk, then went out to a marble bench on the open lawn, a short distance downhill from the shrubbery, to ponder the joined figures and Pippa. For years he had cherished the dream of marrying her, but, knowing that she could not be successfully pursued, he had waited for her to come to him.

The butler placed on a wrought-iron table a glass and a decanter of brandy, which Talcott called his "closest and most soft-spoken friend," and returned to the house. Enjoying a faint breeze drifting down the valley and the shimmering moonbeams on the river, Talcott reflected that Pippa must have drawn the figures with joined hands to prepare him for her willingness to join him in marriage. But for Pippa such an act was out of character. There must be another explanation.

The verb "join" kept popping up in his mind. Abruptly he remembered. Three months previous he had convicted of first degree murder a desperate man who somewhat resembled an ape. The judge had sentenced him to be hanged on the Fourth of July. As the bailiffs were leading him out he had shaken his manacled fists at Talcott and shouted, "Talcott, if I have to return from the grave, you'll join me in death."

Hence the joined hands and the disappearing vagrant. Talcott started, then relaxed. The vagrant must have been a confederate. The convict couldn't possibly escape from the death cell in Albany prison. Talcott poured another glass of brandy, sipped it, and concentrated on the moonbeams dancing in the wake of a lighted excursion boat. Then he heard a low growl that made him feel as if powerful hands were joining on the back of his neck.

"Talcott, you're on your way. I won't be joining you for a long time."

Without turning, Talcott tossed the contents of his glass of brandy over his right shoulder at where he guessed the convict's face would be and sprang from the bench to escape a descending blow. As he did so, a sibilant missile came from a more distant part of the shrubbery and struck somewhere behind Talcott with a sharp thud. A sudden threshing in the bushes was punctuated by another thud and a crash.

Talcott took three hasty steps forward and turned.

Close to a well-rounded arbor vitae behind which she had been concealed stood Pippa in a white mull dress. A short, white jacket covered her shoulders and the two leather holsters for the heavy knives she carried beneath her armpits. Stooping, she retrieved one knife from a prostrate man whose boots projected from beneath a bush. Gathering her skirt she swept across the lawn to where the apeman lay doubled and bleeding. As she picked up her knife, she gave him another solid whack on the head. Taking the glass from Talcott she refilled and returned it.

"Drink it, Mr. Talcott. You are shaking like a leaf." Reaching beneath the marble bench she picked up a deer's foot hunting knife, then slipped it over her shoulder, but beneath her jacket, into a holster slung down her back between her shoulder blades. "That's my utility knife. As I was standing by the river watching an excursion boat, these two hoodlums walked by me, turned, and suddenly came at me. I made a swordsman's thrust at the ape, cut him a little, but he got the knife away from me. They both ran up here, and I followed and hid. I supposed that they were friends of yours until I saw the apeman step out of the bushes behind you waving my knife with evident intent. They're lucky, for I could as easily have killed both of them **with blade strikes instead of the butt. Now call someone to** come with ropes and truss them, and someone else to go for the sheriff."

Still shaking, despite the brandy, Talcott complied and had a chair brought from the house for Pippa. The servants dragged the criminals into the house and, having bound them, stood guard pending arrival of the sheriff.

On the lawn Talcott continued to drink brandy while he compared the moonbeams on the water with the reflection in the masses of Pippa's golden hair. Finally he drew a deep breath and said,

"Pippa, you saved my life. I convicted that man of murder. When sentenced to the gallows, he swore in the courtroom that he would kill me. He is to hang on July Fourth."

"Oh wonderful. Now I'm glad I gave him the butt instead of the blade. All of the holiday people with their picnic baskets will still have the pleasure of watching him hang. Will they have a band playing the death march as he drags his chained feet to the gallows?"

Talcott muttered, "Frontier idea of classical music." Aloud he said, "I don't know what brought you here, but since reading your letter I have tried to believe that you will listen to my proposal of marriage."

After a pause Pippa said quietly, "Four years ago I thought I couldn't live without you. But I had to, and I did. Now I am managing very well."

"Then you no longer love me?"

"I've outgrown it. Now, I'd like to explain why I came here. You, Mr. Talcott, are the only man with enough power and prestige to get DeWitt Clinton nominated for governor by the People's Party. As you must know, they are holding a nominating convention at the Court House in Utica about the middle of August."

"Quite impossible. They will nominate their leader Tallmadge, or John Taylor of Saratoga."

"Confidentially, Taylor won't accept the nomination.

Tallmadge can't if you have previously persuaded him to accept the position of lieutenant governor on Clinton's ticket. Of course, when Van Buren hears about it he'll have you fired from your office of attorney general and drop you from the Regency besides. I know I'm asking a lot of you, but I have a strong reason."

"And the reason?"

"Well, I love the Irish. Not any particular Irishman, but all of them."

"The man you saved me from an hour ago is half Irish."

"Even he, serving under McShane, might have been converted into a useful citizen."

"McShane? They say that he's become quite a successful contractor because of his ability to overcome all sorts of obstacles. Tell me about him and his Irishmen."

In a low tone Pippa spoke slowly, "McShane is rough and tough, but beneath that he's a good shepherd watching over his people. He sees to it that they have better food and more per man than he does. He's the first out in the morning and the last in at night. If the roof leaks, he sleeps under the drip. The men sleep where it's dry. If a man is hurt, he binds up the wound as best he can, does the man's work as long as he can and still boss the job, and subtracts nothing from the man's pay. If later the same man revolts or shirks, McShane will bang him with his fists until the man howls for mercy. Then, if the man volunteers that he is sorry, McShane gives him a paper of pipe tobacco, a jug of whiskey, a kick in the pants, and tells him to work and hurry up about it. When there is danger, McShane always leads the way."

"Where does he find so many men who will put up with that sort of treatment?"

"They're mostly Irish, but a few are Welsh. A handful are of uncertain origin. Ten Irishmen came with him from Tipperary, but all of the other Irish came from jails, mainly in New York City. They were being held for every crime in the book. They had become social and civil outcasts—incorrigibles."

"A strange lot from which to recruit a work force."

"McShane doesn't think so. He calls them his 'emeralds.' He says that men have to dig through a lot of rocks in the mountains of India to find emeralds. They are rare and hard to come by, but so worthwhile."

"Presumably in Ireland many of those jewels ran with organized gangs of thieves and may have had a nodding acquaintance with Irish jails?"

"I doubt it. But if so, they had cause. Irishmen love to get ahead. They'll work and endure as long as there is hope of advancement. In Ireland they were under severe restraint. By contrast, enforcement of our laws is so lax that each American does his own enforcing of what he believes to be the law. Men fight regularly on the streets with fists and canes and on the duelling grounds with swords and pistols.

"During the last six years thousands of Irishmen have landed in New York. Lucky ones have found work. The unlucky, after drifting about seeking work, finally in self preservation have drifted into crime. At first they just stole food. Then, as they felt the thrill of danger—and the Irish thrive on danger—they stole articles of greater value.

"In their course they soon found it expedient to operate in gangs. Through gang wars they divided the city until each gang's territory had its boundaries laid out according to streets. New York citizens regarded the unlucky Irish as equivalent to tigers on the loose, trapped them, and beat them with canes. Before long scores of Irish boys were lodged in jail. Once behind prison doors they were called incorrigibles. When discharged, they found every man's hand against them. Crime then became their only hope of livelihood; that is, until McShane appeared.

"With the Governor's conditional pardon, that they serve out their sentences working for McShane and that they be remanded if they refuse to work for him or obey his orders,

McShane got them out. He had to agree to provide them with food and shelter, but only token wages. McShane paid them the full prevailing wage rate. Whenever it became necessary, he licked them into submission with his fists singly or in pairs until they understood that he was boss. Then he taught them discipline and led them against the challenge of the wilderness."

Talcott poured another glass of brandy. "Sounds like Julius Caesar and his Roman legions. After they had won all of the foreign wars the question arose as to what he would do with them. What will McShane do with *his* men after the canal has been built, especially those who have not yet served out their time?"

"Unlike the Roman soldiers, McShane's men have learned the wholesome lessons that hardship, toil, and frustration teach those who brave the frontier. And that is something that penalties and corrective punishments could never have accomplished, especially with the Irish. As for what they will do, I'll add the two words, 'for us.' Our big cities are still infested with crime. Men are still attacking each other on the streets. Right now in your own home two captured criminals are still waiting for the sheriff. We need more law enforcement officers; and with their experience in crime and their courage, McShane's men might make excellent policemen. When McShane no longer has any work for them, he will see that they have that opportunity.

"But that's not the only opportunity. We have heard that in another year or so Stephen Van Rensselaer plans to endow a school in Troy* where boys can study to become engineers. Because of their practical experience in canal building I'm sure that some of his men will be admitted. Others will study in the offices of lawyers and eventually

---

* Now Rensselaer Polytechnic Institute.

be admitted to the bar. Still others will become physicians and teachers, fight our wars, and help run our local and state governments.

"So, Mr. Talcott, since Dame Fortune has been so kind as to cast many emeralds into our lap, shall we set them in the crown of our goddess Liberty? Or shall we throw them away?"

Talcott put down his glass and extended a hand. Pippa took it, and they sat in silent communion until the arrival of the sheriff and his associates shattered the stillness. After they had gone, Talcott took both of Pippa's hands and looking deep into her sparkling blue eyes said quietly,

"Very well, Pippa. I'll do as you request. Have no concern for adverse effects upon me in consequence. I know those politicians and how to deal with them. In years to come, when I am gone and you have become a grandmother, you may truthfully tell your grandchildren that Pippa Post in a moonlit garden speaking in her sincere, unaffected way made one man understand the Irish and what they can mean to our country—and started the re-election of DeWitt Clinton."

Pippa withdrew her hands, clasped them around his neck, and kissed him. "Goodnight, Mr. Talcott. I know myself better than you do. I wouldn't have made you a good wife. You'll be much happier without me."

"And if I wish to find you, where shall I look?"

Pippa on her way to the garden gate turned. "Somewhere on the canal line in the Mountain Ridge Cut. Any Irishman will tell you where to find me. Please come if you can. I want you to meet McShane."

Talcott listened to the tapping of her heels on the stone pavement until the taps became faint. Pouring a full glass of brandy from his "closest friend" he muttered, "Maybe she's right, at that."

*   *   *   *

CANVASS WHITE

In September of 1824 Nathan Roberts finished digging the channel to the eastern foot of Mountain Ridge. The locks were ready. The channel through Mountain Ridge had already been cut through the rock at the proper depth. Except for inward slopes in the stone tow path and certain bumps on the channel floor it was ready. The twelve-foot-deep earth cutting from the western foot to the fork of Tonawanda Creek had revealed a stone floor. Post holes ten-inches deep had to be drilled in that floor to hold the piles which pressed the retaining planks against the soggy, earth walls. Top anchors made a strong and adequate construction. Still, at that depth earth removal had been slow. The summer of 1825 would be needed to finish the earth cutting. Post-hole drilling, and channel smoothing in Mountain Ridge Cut, would be continued through late fall and winter.

Canvass White had bought for his own use a small wood-burning steamboat in which he cruised up and down the canal in performance of his duties. Shortly after the November election which made DeWitt Clinton Governor and Tallmadge Lieutenant Governor by the largest plurality on record, White found it necessary to visit Mountain Ridge and invited Talcott to go along as guest.

Persuaded but not quite convinced that Pippa would not make him a good wife, Talcott was impelled mainly by curiosity and accepted the invitation. Having fulfilled his promise to cause the nomination of Clinton, and knowing that Pippa was a conscientious and honest girl, he was sure that she would accept if he asked her—even though she felt she "would not make him a good wife." But would he ask her?

When White, carrying a thick coil of half-inch rope, and Talcott, in his usual gray suit with matching cape and beaver, left the boat at the foot of the ridge a cold drenching rain was sweeping in from Lake Ontario. Having climbed to the crest of the slippery ridge, they picked their way along the rock-littered berm side of the channel. As they walked on, White kept close to the edge. Talcott was well ahead, but away from the edge. Suddenly White called out. Talcott approached the edge cautiously and looked down. Beside him a big jagged rock teetered on the edge. Below, Pippa in man's clothing and a battered felt hat squatted holding a drill to which she gave a quarter turn after each blow from the sledge. A burly man with torn shirt and ragged breeches half-tucked into worn boots swung the sledge.

White quickly tied one end of his rope to a tree, then slung the coil across the top of the rock to Talcott. Together they whipped the rope outward and across the face of the rock. Talcott carried his end to the nearest tree and tied it. Almost immediately the rope became taut. The rock had started sliding on the slippery clay. In a short time it would have fallen on McShane and Pippa.

White was down on hands and knees wedging the rock back with shattered fragments. From the other side Talcott followed his example. When they stood up White shouted,

"McShane, you'd better have this rock pulled back. Another minute and it would have fallen on both of you."

Without looking up or interrupting his swing, McShane replied, "Sure I've been watching it all morning. I've sent two of the lads to find a team of oxen and drag it back to safety. They should be up there by now."

Far to the southwest through the trees Talcott saw the oxen approaching. Turning his back on them, he retraced his steps eastward. White hurried after him.

"Hey, what's the matter? I wanted to introduce you to McShane."

Talcott continued walking. "You have."

"Your face is as white as a sheet."

"I can believe it. That's the way I feel."

"But why?"

"When you love a woman and you see a rock the size of that one sliding down on her, and the man with her not even pulling her away to safety and she not doing anything about it either—"

"Well?"

"If she's perfectly willing to die with him, she's willing to live with him. In other words she's ready to marry him. There can be only one top man in a woman's life. There may be other men, but they'll all rate below that top one. In Pippa's life it's McShane. The rain is falling like anything, and I'm soaked. I've seen all I wish to see. Let's get back to your boat."

Aboard the boat Talcott poured two glasses from his "closest friend," which he had had the forethought to bring along. White raised a glass and said,

"Here's to Pippa and to your broken heart for the beautiful girl you have loved and lost—my sympathy."

Talcott refilled both glasses and raised his. "And here's to McShane who has won what I've lost. But sometimes it's better to have loved and lost than—never to have lost at all."

"I can believe it. That's the way I feel."

"But why?"

"When you love a woman and you see a rose the face of that one sliding down on her, told the man with her not even pulling her away to safety, and she not doing anything about it either—"

"Well?"

"If she's perfectly willing to die with him, she's willing to live with him. In other words she's ready to marry him. There can be only one one man in a woman's life. There may be other men, but the devil fall take low that top one. In Tippa's life it's McShane. The man is falling hee anything, and I'm sorted. I've seen all I want to see. Let's get back to your home."

Aboard the boat Falcon poured two glasses from his "closest friend," which he had had the forethought to bring along. White made a glass and said:

"Here's to Tippa and to your broken heart for the beautiful girl you have loved and lost—my sympathy."

Falcon nodded. He clinked and raised his. "And here's to McShane who has won what I've lost. But sometimes it's better to have loved and lost than never to have lost at all."

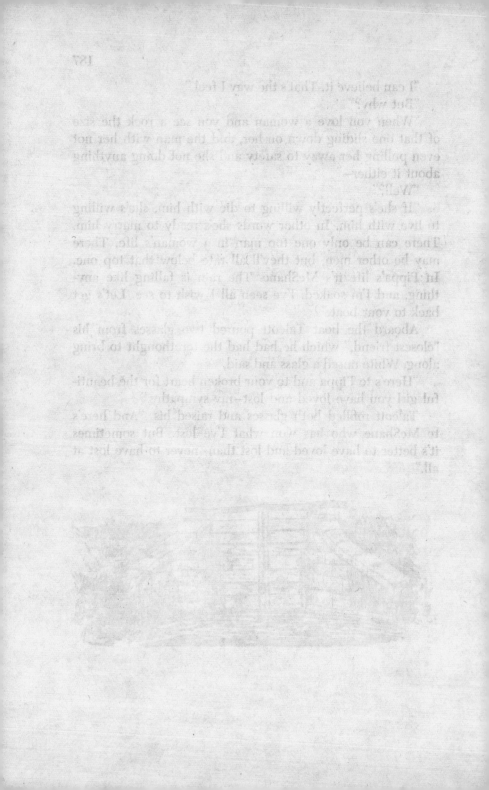

BIBLIOGRAPHY

Bagg, M. M. *Pioneers of Utica*. Utica, N. Y.: Curtiss and Childs, 1877.

Bradbury, Anna. *History of the City of Hudson*. Hudson, N. Y.: Record Printing and Publishing Co., 1908.

Edmonds, Walter D. *The First Hundred Years*. Oneida Community, N. Y.: Oneida Ltd., 1935.

Ellis, Franklin. *History of Columbia County*. Philadelphia, Pa.: Everts & Ensign, 1878.

Johnson, Willis Fletcher, and Smith, Ray B. *Political and Governmental History of New York*. vols. 1 & 2. Syracuse, N. Y.: Syracuse Press, Inc., 1922.

Jones, Pomeroy. *Annals and Recollections of Oneida County*. Rome, N. Y.: Pomeroy Jones, 1851.

Weise, Arthur James. *History of the City of Troy*. Troy, N. Y.: W. H. Young, 1876.

Whitford, Noble. *History of New York State Canals*. Albany, N. Y.: Brandon Printing Co., 1906.

Transactions of the Oneida County Historical Society. vols. 1 & 2. Utica, N. Y.: Ellis H. Roberts & Co., Printers, 1881, 1885.

The Surveying of the Canal Route. (Reports of the New York State Canal Commissioners.) Albany, N. Y.: N. Y. State Canal Commissioners, 1816.

The Annual Report of the Progress of Construction. (Reports of the New York State Canal Commissioners.) Albany, N. Y.: N. Y. State Canal Commissioners, 1818-1826.

Pamphlets

Campbell, Wallace Hamilton. *Canastota and the Erie Canal*. Onondaga County Savings Bank.

———. *In the Erie Canal Days*. Onondaga County Savings Bank.

McKelvey, Blake. *Rochester History*, vol. IX, 3 & 4.

———. *Rochester and the Erie Canal*.

Wright, R. N. *Bottoming Out*. New York State Canal Society. Nos. 15, 16, 17, 18, 19, 21, 22.

The Erie Canal. Utica, N. Y.: Munson-Williams-Proctor Institute.

8/20/21

Pulaski

Oswego

Oswego R.

ONEIDA R.

ThreeRivers

ONEIDA LAKE

Fish Cr.

Wood Cr.

Rome

Nine Mile Cr.

ERIE

W. Canada Cr.

Oneida

UTICA

Herkimer

Weedsport

COSSITS   CORS

(SYRACUSE)

Limestone Cr. Feeder

Chittenango Cr. Feeder

Cansesy Cr.

ORISKANY CR.

SKANEATELES L.

OTISCO L.

Butternut Cr. Feeder

Cazenovia

OTSEGO L.

Cooperstown

Cortland

Tioughnioga R.

Otselic Ck.

Chenango R.

Unadilla River

Oneonta

Susquehanna R.

Susquehanna

River

Binghamton

W. Br. Delaware R.

Delaware

Delaware R.